The Parlour Song Book

The Parlour Song Book

A Casquet of Vocal Gems

Edited and introduced by

MICHAEL R. TURNER

The music edited by ANTONY MIALL

'Sing me the songs that to me were so dear,
Long, long ago, long ago'

MICHAEL JOSEPH

1.

First published in Great Britain by Michael Joseph Ltd
52 Bedford Square, London, WC1
1972

Filmset in Photon Imprint 11 on 12 pt. by
Richard Clay (The Chaucer Press), Ltd, Bungay, Suffolk
and printed in Great Britain by
Fletcher & Son, Ltd, Norwich

Acknowledgements

My sincere thanks go to 'the onlie begetters' of this book, Mr Noel Morton and the late Mr Roy Giles. It was their sympathetic performances of many Victorian ballads that set me off collecting and discovering. A number of first editions of songs were found in that Aladdin's Cave for the musician, the BBC Music Library in London, and I am therefore particularly grateful to Mr John Meloy, the Librarian, for his interest and patience. The Music Collection of the New York Public Library was another treasure house of information where my inquiries were answered with quiet efficiency. Most of all, however, I must thank the Music Editor of this book Mr Antony Miall for his unquenchable enthusiasm.

I am grateful to those publishers who have granted permission to use copyright material and to the Performing Rights Society who helped enormously in tracing who owns which rights. Despite their aid, however, and other careful investigation it has not been possible to locate the copyright holders of one or two songs. To these I offer my apologies. I must also thank Clarkson Potter for permission to quote an excerpt from 'Moving Picture Cowboy' which appears in the collection *Cowboy and Western Songs* by Austin E. and Alta S. Fife.

It is only proper, too, to acknowledge the artists whose designs decorate the section titles. These illustrations, mostly lithographs, all come from nineteenth-century sheet music, English and American. The charm and verve of these 'song fronts' are an especial bonus for the collector of Victorian music.

M. R. T.

Contents

Contents

Contents

Introduction

I

That extravagant Victorian, Sir George Sitwell, reports his son Osbert, was looking down upon a two-year-old infant slumbering in his perambulator. 'I do hope,' he remarked in sentimental tones, 'that they won't forget to teach the little man to sing after dinner. Nothing makes a man so popular.'

Nothing, indeed made young man or maiden more acceptable in the genteel drawing-room than the possession of a melodious voice and an ability to play upon the pianoforte well, but not too well. The songs they rendered were as decorous and refined as their exponents. Ronald Firbank, a little after our period, summed up in *Vainglory* the feel of those evenings when, the plush drapes drawn across the windows, the gaslight throwing its warm glow on china-pink faces and silky whiskers, the palms and pampas grass casting gently shifting shadows upon the embossed wallpaper, the hostess suggested:

'Well, won't somebody go to the piano?'

'Miss Wookie will,' her mother said. 'Won't you, Kate? And perhaps sing some little song besides. She knows such shoals. What was that one, my dear, that despairing dismal one about the heliotrope? "When Heliotropes Turn Back". It's the true story of a sailor. Or he might have been a coastguard. And he goes away. And he comes back. And, of course, he finds her dead.'

If that were all that parlour balladry could provide, then one has no choice but to agree wholeheartedly with those critics who find most middle-class song so unutterably vapid that they can scarcely bear to mention it. Kenneth Young has made an affectionate condemnation of these 'little songs': 'The essence of the Victorian ballad was to be lightly sentimental, lightly religious and lightly gay. Essentially they were nostalgic, not dramatic; they were intended to raise a slight sigh after the port and cigars, not a *crise des nerfs*; they were the antithesis of the brooding intelligence and psychological penetration of the songs of Hugo Wolf.' That is so, but it is well to remember that the pleasures of social intercourse in the days before radio and television could properly include other elements than the profundities of Germanic composers.

The trouble with the conventional judgements upon Victorian song is that they suppose a constant uninspiring level of unambitious music presenting unremarkable sentiments. They disregard the captivating charm and melodiousness of many of the ballads, the sheer enjoyment with which they can be performed, even today, and the whole intriguing ambiance of nineteenth-century society that they conjure up. Such judgements disregard, too, the real if ambivalent delights that may be derived from good bad music.

To discuss the artistic life of the bourgeoisie in terms other than contempt is still unfashionable. 'Folk' art, which is seen as the sturdy, vital production of the salt of the earth, its working class, is almost universally regarded as being the only worthwhile part of popular culture. The study of intellectual art is another matter, of course, for this engages the higher faculties and encourages pleasurable if rigorous cerebration. That

1

group of people, too materially comfortable to be part of the favoured proletariat and supremely uninterested in the agonies of the intellectual, is almost totally neglected. One can see the attitude in the work of admirable and balanced scholars. Hans Nathan, whose *Dan Emmett and the Rise of Early Negro Minstrelsy* is a model of unstuffy scholarship, states almost as a matter of course that it is the early, vigorous folk aspects of the subject that interest him; he does not investigate what happened to the Minstrels when they began to find their most responsive audience in the middle class. Let us hope that some day he will.

For the full understanding of the nineteenth century, however, the views and tastes of the backbone of the English-speaking nations, the merchant and professional classes, should be considered. This book has no scholarly pretentions and contains little original research. It does, however, try to gather together some highly significant strands of Victorian life and exhibit them in a manner that may help understanding of a very complicated and rapidly developing era.

It was an era of delight in music, when people made their own pleasures. With the growth of education came an insatiable demand for the means to indulge newly acquired tastes and newly developed talents. The music critic of *The Times*, Francis Hueffer, remarked in 1877: 'It is no exaggeration to say that with the exception perhaps of natural science ... there is no branch of human knowledge, or of human art, in which the change that the half-century of the Queen's reign has seen is so marked as it is in the love of music.' Two sets of statistics will indicate the quickening pace. The United States of America manufactured 2,500 pianofortes in 1829, over 9,000 in 1851, 21,000 in 1860, and in 1910 the annual total was a thundering 370,000. Music teachers were needed to provide performers for this army of instruments, and the British census figures for musicians and music masters were for 1881 25,546, an increase of 38% on 1871; in 1901 there were 43,249, and in 1911 the nation supported a melodious 47,116.

Without the pianoforte the astonishing rise of genteel domestic music would probably have been much slower. The engineers of the industrial revolution came to the aid of the musician with the upright or cottage piano. This (and later and to a lesser extent the harmonium, the pedestrian organ and other ingenious American derivatives) was a nineteenth-century status symbol to which the family climbing the social ladder inevitably aspired. Some of the well-to-do even became two-piano families. Towards the middle of the century the more developed upright piano began to replace the square, and the more expensive examples attracted the talents of enthusiastic if unrestrained craftsmen in rosewood, mahogany, walnut and other favourite woods. Inlaid with ivory or brass, decorated with marquetry or ormolu, the piano was a testimony, as is the bechromed automobile today, of a family's standing. In its most exotic form, with ball-and-claw feet and luxuriant carved foliage, it could be admired at the Great Exhibition of 1851, but humbler versions could be purchased upon the instalment system for a mere thirty guineas. It should be remembered, however, that thirty guineas was the equivalent of a domestic servant's full annual wage.

For those unable to afford a piano there was on offer the invention of the clever Daniel Hewitt, which provided all the advantages of the instrument without the expense of a case. According to a patent taken out in 1854, the strings of the instrument were attached to the wall of a room. Although ingenious, the idea apparently did not catch on, unlike some of the other myriad improvements and variations of the period. The scope of the pianoforte was extended until it almost became a substitute for full orchestra, with stops to simulate cymbals, harp, bassoon and harpsichord. Some machines were fitted with a swell pedal that progressively lifted the lid in imitation of the organ swell.

2

It was inevitable that, in the 1850s, the piano and the organ should be merged into one magnificent 'organo-piano', bringing a touch of the cathedral into the drawing-room.

The dulcet and eminently respectable notes of the reed organ were to be heard increasingly as the century proceeded. The harmonium, handy version of the King of Instruments, could cost as little as ten guineas. Encased in a heavy cabinet of intricate Gothic splendour it was certain of a ready market in the more devout households where it reinforced the note of sober piety at family prayers. If it could be used upon less serious occasions as well, so much the better. In the song 'Maggie Murphy's Home', it is the proud possession of an Irish immigrant family in New York City:

> There's an organ in the parlor
> To give the house a tone,
> And you're welcome ev'ry evening
> At Maggie Murphy's home.

The slowness of the harmonium's speech made the rapid passagework which characterised contemporary piano music out of the question. The instrument found its true role in hymn and song accompaniments. Indeed, it is a revelation to hear some of Sullivan's songs accompanied by the domestic organ and piano together. The passages of quasi-recitative in his more ecclesiastically inclined songs are much more aptly accompanied by the harmonium than by the piano, although both instruments were required in the original setting of 'The Lost Chord'. Many popular composers, like Sullivan, wrote especially for the harmonium and the larger and many-stopped American organ. Their works were certain of a wide circulation for neither organ nor piano remained decorative and idle in the parlour. They were the hub around which the family's social life revolved.

The new musicians, amateur as they may have been, required new music to play upon their glistening new pianofortes and harmoniums. The rude melodies of the street and the farm were naturally ignored in favour of the polite forms of music formerly the preserve of the moneyed classes in the previous century. A fresh public, bringing from its non-conformist origins a muscular morality and distaste for both vulgarity and aristocratic libertinism, developed from that polite music an original and refined type of melody unlike anything before it.

A modest musical ability became essential to polite young men and women, just as it had been three or four hundred years before. In the Tudor period, everyone of any social pretention at all was expected to be able to sing; he who could not read his part in a madrigal was considered no true gentleman. Through the sixteenth and seventeenth centuries music *qua* music continued as a private pleasure. Except for sacred music and masque and opera there were no public performances of music in London until 1672. As a social emollient, however, it still reigned supreme. Samuel Pepys, that hard-working civil servant, played several instruments well and could arrange, compose and sing. The following century saw the rise of the professional musician and despite the foundation of many singing societies, some convivial, some, like the Madrigal Society, serious, the amateur singer retired into the background. The more sober went so far as to warn their offspring of the social perils of music. Lord Chesterfield, for instance, advised his son never to participate in the art, for 'it puts a gentleman in a very frivolous and contempt-ible light'. The beginning of the nineteenth century brought a change, an enormous resurgence of amateur performance.

3

Once more, everyone sang. They sang in their homes, they sang duets, part songs and glees in groups, and they sang in crowds. Hundreds of choral societies were born and nearly as many died in Britain in the nineteenth century, only to survive as an official-looking stamp on a dusty copy of 'Messiah' in a second-hand bookshop. Choral singing became a national sport, and its history is a fascinating one. One can only pause here to recognise its importance as a force with immense impetus.

Everyone sang, and subsidiary musical industries proliferated. Music teaching, music publishing and even musical medicine boomed. A new interest in the function of the vocal chords led to a stream of books by surgeons. Lozenges, Italian cordials for improving the voice and exercise books all enjoyed wide public favour. Patently (and patented) absurd methods were used, found wanting and discarded. Plums were put into the mouth to stop the cheeks touching the teeth, thus augmenting the sound produced. Weights were loaded on the chest while the enthusiastic indulged in breathing exercises. It seems as if there were almost as many methods to improve singing as there were singers. It was obviously a considerable social impediment to be born tone-deaf.

All this activity, of course, did not guarantee high standards. The fact that the qualities of amateur performance, however well-meaning, have not changed over the years can be confirmed by an item from the *Musical Times* of August 1893: 'The critic of *The West Wilts Herald* . . . remarks that two young ladies gave a new recital of a duet and adds: "It is a pity that Blumenthal did not leave directions as to how flat he really did want it sung." '

It could not last. As the century drew to a close, teachers and others were already beginning to lament an apparent falling-off in musical devotion. One insidious rival was the bicycle. By 1896 the *Musical Times* was complaining of its fatal fascination: 'There are literally thousands of young ladies whose leisure hours, formerly passed in large part on the music-stool, are now spent in the saddle of the "iron bird" as a lady journalist has poetically described the bicycle.' Pianos were being sold to pay for the seductive new machine, and 'it is alleged that, after bicycling for any length of time, many ladies find their wrists ache so much as to render pianoforte playing well-nigh impossible'. It was the same in the United States, and the spring concert season of that year 'suffered materially from the prevailing cult of the bicycle'. Some authorities saw dangers for the voice, and Madame Mathilde Marchesi, of Leipzig, declared that 'the rapid passage through the air may be a positive source of danger'. Music, in fact, was suffering from the contemporary manifestations of women's liberation.

But this was all in the future. During most of the century music, and especially vocal music, had no rival as a middle-class occupation.

It became an important factor in mating customs. Young ladies could show off their genteel accomplishments on the pianoforte and young men could throw out a manly chest as they rendered a tenor ballad, both performing the courting displays necessary for the continuance of the race. Social restrictions demanded that a maiden should be closely chaperoned: it was only with the help of the piano and parlour song that she could conduct a discreet correspondence of timorous smiles, fluttering eyelashes and significant blushes with her lover. A melodious voice was a decided asset in the Victorian marriage market, and an ability to perform upon the family piano a skill to be gained as early as possible in childhood.

Musical education became an obsession in both America and Britain. In the States, the traditional Yankee singing masters, who laid the foundations for the nineteenth-century explosion, had to give place to the latest fashions in music teaching at the same time as new fads in clothes and manners were sweeping the nation. In the 'thirties and

4

'forties the old fa-sol-la system was gradually superseded by the European do-re-mi method that represented 'scientific improvement'. In England the great spread of teaching singing in schools was given impetus by the Reverend John Curwen's Tonic Sol-Fa method; his ideas appealed particularly to the emergent non-conformist middle class and the artistic side of musical education came, upon occasions, quite definitely second to its moral and religious aspects. *The Tonic Sol-Fa Reporter* was constantly giving its readers solemn advice about avoiding sinful frivolity and even inveighed against the wearing of low dresses in public—'The dreadful tide of this fashion comes from France.' The Reverend H. R. Haweis, who wrote an immensely popular mid-Victorian text, *Music and Morals*, agreed that 'certain musical forms have the power of inducing in us a preference for wholesome rather than unworthy attitudes, and of encouraging balanced and reasonable judgements'.

Haweis is a key figure to the understanding of the Victorian view of music. His book still makes good reading, for he was no bigot and took a perhaps untypical delight in the performances of street musicians and the fare provided by penny gaffs and song and supper rooms, the nurseries of music-hall. Nevertheless, he was convinced that the quality of music was linked directly to the private lives of the men who wrote it:

> . . . it is . . . noteworthy that so many great composers have been men whose emotions were so severely disciplined, and whose lives were so regulated, that they stand as examples not only of steady and indefatigable workers, but also of high-minded, moral and even religious men.

It is natural, therefore, that he should have found 'the essentially voluptuous character of Italian music' and 'the essentially frivolous and sentimental character of French music' decidedly inferior to 'the essentially moral, many sided, and philosophical character of German music'. A feature of his book is a survey of the religious practices and moral worth of the great composers, on his way round the exhibits mentioning with approval that Papa Haydn . . . 'never began writing his compositions without the words "In nomine Domine", and that whenever he found it difficult to compose, he would resort to his rosary in prayer—a practice which he declared was always accompanied by the happiest results.' Such laudable conduct excused his possibly 'more than Platonic . . . relations with a certain Mademoiselle Boselli'. Scarlatti, Haweis noted, worked in a charity school; Gluck, although in his declining years 'somewhat addicted to drinking', had previously set a good example to the dissolute city of Paris; dear old Sebastian Bach was a good husband; Handel was of unquestioned personal purity; Mozart attended mass with his future wife; Beethoven's integrity was spotless; and Mendelssohn showed his moral quality by strongly disapproving of a scene in *Fra Diavolo* in which 'a young lady divests herself of her garments and sings a song to the effect that next day at this time she will be married'. These admirable composers were rewarded by being 'remarkably healthy and long-lived', with certain unfortunate exceptions whose noble lives were shortened by the 'unfair and pitiless conditions' imposed by society.

Such was the context in which parlour songs were written and enjoyed. It is little wonder that they express uniformly uplifting sentiments and reflect the teachings of the Protestant ethic. The Reverend Haweis, incidentally, was particularly scathing on the subject of drawing-room ballads, but it was the royalty system that financed them as much as the apparent meretriciousness of their style that drew his indignant fire. Songs by 'true English musicians' like Arthur Sullivan he commended heartily; we would now find little essential difference between Sullivan's 'The Lost Chord' and other vocal gems of his time.

Songs were seen not only to have improving effects in a comparatively passive sense. They came to hand in many hard-fought battles for social and moral betterment. The campaigns in which they served included some of the most weighty causes of the century, among them abolition, temperance, female emancipation and the fight against poverty. In the bitter controversy over slavery in the years leading up to the American Civil War, for instance, ballads were written and sung with intense passion by the protagonists for both sides. There were many songs in support of the message of Harriet Beecher Stowe's *Uncle Tom's Cabin*, a novel that did more than any other single literary work to raise the tide of international indignation against slavery. The tone of the novel may have been extravagantly sentimental and over-emphatic ('Whip me till the blood runs down,' sobbed little Topsy), but it caught and held contemporary enthusiasm. Ballads like 'Uncle Tom's Religion' supported the theme:

> Patient here I'll go to glory,
> There is comfort for the slave,
> When de lash makes dis flesh gory
> I'll pray to him who died to save.

Southern songs in riposte included jeers at the character of Mrs Stowe, their writers summoning up a corrosive strain that fully equalled Northern vituperation. The proselytising Hutchinsons, the earnest family troupe of singers whom we shall meet frequently in these pages, carried their melodious propaganda to Northern troops. So excessive were they in their zeal that General McLellan expelled them from the Army of the Potomac during one of their tours, with the stricture that the war had other objects as well as abolition. President Lincoln, significantly, reversed his order.

It is noteworthy that the author of *Uncle Tom's Cabin* was a woman. The nineteenth century brought with it an increasingly militant female movement. While the genteel young lady was required to behave within the strait-jacket of decorum, women of strong character were for ever breaking out. They turned their attentions, inevitably, to social reform of many kinds: Mrs Bloomer and Florence Nightingale were sisters under their divided skirts and crinolines, they were just the leaders of a great crusade. Women increasingly took over the temperance movement, they campaigned against slum conditions, they fought for exploited children. America, particularly, with its ever expanding frontiers that took men away from the family for years at a time, was tending towards matriarchy. Women were beginning to get a liking for ruling society, and it was their feminine craving for gentility, their fear of the rough and popular combined with lack of understanding of the artistically sophisticated that dictated parlour tastes. They might admire their dynamic sisters from a safe distance, but it was the comfortably safe middle-class women who imposed politeness, sentimentality, conventionality and superficiality upon a basically raw and lusty society like a veneer. Their music was the drawing-room ballad.

II

The broad Atlantic has, indeed, become a mere pond. The wooden vessel looks almost as antique as the caracks of the Armada. Iron has come to rule supreme; steam has made the picturesque sails of sixty years ago as old fashioned as the trireme.

Introduction

Sir Walter Besant was writing in the Diamond Jubilee number of the *Illustrated London News*, comparing the England of 1897 with that of 1837. He celebrated not only the advances in technology, but the greater speed and efficiency of communications. Those who complain dismally today of the coming of a trans-Atlantic culture should be reminded that the beginnings lie as far back as a century and a half ago. Songs voyaged back and forth across the ocean then as regularly if not quite as swiftly as the melodies of American musicals or the effusions of the latest English pop group do today. At first, as was inevitable, the movement was mainly westward, but by the late 1830s real exchange was taking place. Operas and melodramas started songs off on their careers on both sides of the Atlantic, and the travels of such entertainers as Henry Russell, who wrote many of his best ballads in America, and 'Daddy' Rice, who took 'Jim Crow' and other black-face songs to London and Paris, contributed to the growth of an international musical taste. The pace of exchange was faster than one might think today: the very first Minstrel troupe toured Britain within a few months of its premiere in New York in 1843, harbinger of the great invasion of Europe by American popular music. An admired poet like Longfellow or Tennyson had scarcely time to blot the ink of his latest offering before eager composers, both British and American, were setting his verses.

The scramble to set new poems by leading bards became somewhat undignified. Even poets of lesser renown, like Mrs Hemans, the Honourable Mrs Norton, Eliza Cook, Thomas Haynes Bayly or Charles Mackay, found the products of their genius in great demand. As for the works of the great, 'Excelsior!' exists not only in the duet form by Balfe included in this collection, but in settings by the indefatigable John Blockley and by the Hutchinson family of New Hampshire; 'Goodnight, Beloved' attracted Balfe again, and also Carl Reinhardt and Ciro Pinsuti, who produced it in a part-song version; 'The Village Blacksmith' hammered to rhythms invented by Reinhardt and W. H. Weiss—and these are only the best-known versions. Quite often, particularly when the ocean safely divided poet and composer, the former received no financial reward for the use of his lyric gem, even if he received an acknowledgement as to authorship, not an invariable courtesy. The current state of copyright law encouraged in the most genteel of the social arts the most ungenteel forms of piracy.

As songs settled in a new country, they rapidly became naturalised. Sometimes, more appropriate lyrics were devised or the originals adapted. Haste was all important, however, and within days of a trans-Atlantic steamer reaching dock music publishers rushed out editions of the ballads it brought, hardly pausing an hour to Americanise or Anglicise the spellings of the words. Many Britons now would be amazed to learn that 'Daisy Bell', the music-hall song that many took to be a satire upon the Prince of Wales's dear friend the Countess of Warwick, is in fact of American origin, as are such completely 'English' pieces as 'Ta-ra-ra Boom-de-ay', 'After the Ball', 'A Bird in a Gilded Cage', 'Silver Threads among the Gold' and 'Where Did You Get That Hat?' Even 'Down at the Old Bull and Bush' derives from a tune by Tin Pan Alley's Harry von Tilzer.

Such two-way trade in popular music does not mean that the parlour songs of each country lacked national character. If the sentiments were similar, for the moral climate in America was much the same (if its excesses were more strongly marked) as in Britain, they were expressed in different ways. The British panoply of upper-middle-class artistic balladry by socially recognised composers—Sir Henry Bishop, Sir Frederic Cowen, Sir Julius Benedict, Sir Joseph Barnby, Sir Francesco Paolo Tosti, Sir Arthur Sullivan—had the flavour of concert platform and oratorio. This was allied to the productions of such raffish theatrical figures as the poets Bunn and Fitzball and decorous musical entertainers, and the offerings of gently-born poetesses and female composers. In America, the frontier society produced simpler, more direct, more passionately written songs. The prohibitionist printer and composer Henry Clay Work is a purely American figure, as are those serious teachers and journalists who turned their hands to the lyre, the democratically-minded lady poets, and the professional actors and singers of black-face Minstrelsy. At the end of the century in America came the fast-living founders of Tin Pan Alley, the first popular composers to carry tear-jerking to such an extent that they ended up by writing with their tongues firmly in their cheeks.

The two nations produced different styles, but each borrowed from the other. The result is a body of song, clearly identifiable in manner and content. Undoubtedly it possesses its own social grades, in descending order from the sedate and serious ballads originally given on the concert platform right down to the humble, if lively, melodies of street musicians. Only the upper ranks, appealing to the middle classes, belong to parlour balladry proper.

III

Many, if not most, parlour songs were not written specifically for the drawing-room. The amateur singer took his material whence he heard it, and the composer and publisher could only reach this eager buyer of sheet music from the public stage. It was the sole means by which new songs could be introduced and, if they struck the audience's fancy, could be popularised. Practically every piece in this book had a public baptism in opera, on the concert platform, at a pleasure-garden, in a ballad concert, sung by an itinerant family troupe, on a show-boat, in a Minstrel show, at a church social or temperance meeting, on a seaside bandstand or in vaudeville or music-hall. Only the last two, because they came at the end of the century and were primarily for the entertainment of the working class, had not acquired the respectability necessary for large-scale incursions into the drawing-room. The stage may have been the wet-nurse of middle-class song, but who thinks now of 'Home! Sweet Home!' as a piece from a melodrama, or 'Beautiful Dreamer' as part of a Minstrel show? They can be recognised instantly by their tone as belonging essentially to family evenings around the piano. Nevertheless, some appreciation of the genesis of parlour ballads on some platform or other is essential for their full enjoyment.

Opera and operetta need little comment. The musical drama in its many forms has always provided the amateur with material and one can assume that it always will. The actual medium may change, from the early nineteenth-century stock melodrama to Gilbert and Sullivan and on to and beyond the Hollywood musical, but show business is always show business and success in it demands an ear on the part of the management for a good song.

One nineteenth-century manifestation, and primarily American, was the highly respectable family troupe of travelling singers. The spread of the socially conscious, highly moral parlour ballad was due in large degree to their efforts. There were dozens of such companies on the road in the States from the 'forties onwards, but they did not arise spontaneously. Their inspiration was without doubt the Tyrolese Rainer Family who toured America in 1838. This Alpine group, two men, two women, singing in four-part harmony, was representative of many troupes who had delighted European countries since the 1820s. They started a tradition that is carried on by the Trapp Family of our time. The troupes of native Americans would appear for one-night stands in churches, theatres, schools or anywhere (except saloons) where an audience could gather. They sang often without accompaniment, but usually to piano, organ or melodeon. The moral uplift of their repertoire was varied by direct sentiment, by strait-laced comedy and by heart-felt patriotism. They exploited, too, that dominant lachrymose strain so characteristic of the period; 'The Lament of the Blind Orphan Girl', 'The Guardians of the Grave' and 'Oh! I'm in Sadness' were a few of the songs that managed to combine morbidity with entertainment.

The leading troupes, while irreproachably respectable, were also highly professional. From the mountains of New Hampshire came the famous Hutchinsons. They gave their first concert at the Baptist meeting-house at Milford in 1839, and John Hutchinson and his brothers set off for Boston to seek culture. There they found their fortune. As well as the usual improving sentimental ballad, they adopted the violently dramatic musical scena with reforming intent, like Henry Russell's 'The Maniac' and 'The Ship on Fire' and Lyman Heath's 'The Snow Storm' (on page 306). Their signature tune was 'The Old Granite State', published by them in 1843:

> We have eight other Brothers,
> And of Sisters, just another,
> Besides our Father, and our Mother,
>   In the 'Old Granite State'.
> With our present number,
> There are fifteen in the tribe,
> Thirteen sons and daughters,
> And their history we bring . . .
>
> David, Noah, Andrew, Zephy (aniah),
> Caleb, Joshua, Jesse and Beny (jamin),
> Judson, Rhoda, John and Asa,
> And Abbe, are our names:
>   We're the sons of Mary,
>   Of the tribe of Jesse,
>   And we now address ye,
> With our native mountain song . . .

They proclaim themselves 'Good old fashion'd singers', and in other verses announce that they despise oppression, are 'friends of emancipation', and, furthermore:

> We are all teetoatlers
> And have sign'd the Temp'rance pledge.

As opponents of the demon drink and champions of liberty, they travelled England and Ireland—Charles Dickens organised a reception for them—and for half a century two generations of Hutchinsons carried their simple faith and honest, straightforwardly sentimental melodies across America to audiences who were never likely to go anywhere near a concert platform.

Female suffrage, abolition, equality, old-time religion and optimistic forecasts of the coming millennium: their subject-matter, as befitted their Biblical names, was of the most lofty order, and it appears that the other family companies, the Bakers, the Barkers, the Hughes, the Alleghenians, the Aeolians, the Orpheans, the Harmoneons and the rest, were of equal probity.

In Britain, there were fewer family troupes, also imitating the Tyrolese Rainers, and their material was attuned to the tastes of the fashionable spa or watering-place at a time when the nation was discovering the curative properties of cold salt water. One such group was the Praeger family, of whom the Reverend Haweis remarked that it was 'not an uncommon thing for them at the close of the Brighton or Folkestone season to deposit several hundred pounds in the bank'. The family troupes were purveyors of moral uplift; the same high level was not the invariable fare provided by other popular entertainers.

The sound of 'Oh, Dem Golden Slippers' with the full force of the calliope (pronounced 'cally-ope') of the *Floating Palace* behind it could be heard for miles as the show-boat tied up at a Mississippi landing stage. The brazen tones of the steam-piano, played with canvas gloves, called more or less delighted frontier audiences to a programme of songs, instrumental acts, dances and burlesques (pronounced 'burly-cues'), or sometimes a performance of Shakespeare, suitably edited, a melodrama, a Minstrel show, a quack doctor's demonstration, perhaps a complete circus and always music. The show-boats were often family affairs. Indeed, the very first, the *Floating Theatre* of 1831, was the invention of the Chapman family, immigrants from England. Other famous river families were the McNairs (with their boat, *New Era*), the Frenches (*French's New Sensation*), the Thoms (*Princess*) and the Reynoldses (*America* and *Majestic*). While some of their programmes were of dubious moral worth, the better show-boats made a strong point of advertising their respectability. They brought melody to people deprived of entertainment, and especially of refined entertainment, and fought the current, grounding, fire and explosion, floating logs, ice, starvation and sometimes hostile audiences to do so. Life on the show-boats was hard, varied and sometimes heroic.

However musical, the show-boats did not give birth to their own style of ballad. Their performers used what came to hand, and that was, very frequently, the songs popularised by black-face Minstrelsy.

One day in 1828, or 1829, or 1830—for the legend is uncertain—a 'ham' actor called Thomas Dartmouth Rice was walking down a street in Cincinatti, Louisville or perhaps Pittsburgh. His eye was caught by an old, or maybe young, crippled or deformed, but certainly ragged, Negro street-performer, or stage-driver, or stevedore, or porter, or stable-boy, executing an odd, limping, shuffling dance and singing:

> Wheel about and turn about and do jis so,
> Eb'ry time I wheel about I jump Jim Crow.

Struck by the comic possibilities of this curious exhibition, 'Daddy' Rice borrowed the Negro's tattered garments, blacked his face and, at the local theatre that evening, did an imitation. It was an instant success, especially as, at the end of the act, the half-naked Negro burst on stage with an anguished demand for his clothes. Rice made himself rich and famous with 'Jim Crow'. He was noted for his use of five- and ten-dollar pieces as buttons for his coat.

Of course, the black-face tradition did not begin so dramatically, although this discovery of 'Jim Crow' himself almost certainly happened. Ancient Greek actors darkened their features with soot, and ever since it has been a constant practice for white performers to black up for the stage. Othello is perhaps the most obvious example, but the eighteenth century saw many noble savages (Thomas Southerne's *Oroonoko* of 1695 was probably the first) and comic Negro servants. Lugubrious slave songs had a mild popularity, some of them in what passed for Negro dialect.

In the early part of the next century mock-Negroes became increasingly popular in the United States, some of their songs, like 'Massa Georgee Washington and General Lafayette' by Micah Hawkins, becoming national favourites, but it was not until 1843 in New York City that black-face performers actually joined together in a troupe.

Four actor friends, Dan Emmett, Frank Brower, Bill Whitlock and Dick Pelham, met in a lodging-house almost by accident and fell to amusing themselves on the humble instruments used in their black-face acts. They tried out their band in a billiard room. So successful were they that the New York press announced for February 6th, at the Bowery Amphitheatre, as part of a normal circus show:

> First Night of the novel, grotesque, original and surpassingly melodious Ethiopian band entitled the *Virginia Minstrels*, being an exclusively musical entertainment combining the banjo, violin, bone castanets and tambourine, and entirely exempt from the vulgarities and other objectionable features which have hitherto characterized Negro extravaganzas.

This was the original Minstrel manifesto, and the myriad troupes of the next sixty years hardly departed from its spirit. The idea of the Minstrel band spread like wildfire. Within months Dan Emmett and the Virginia Minstrels were performing in England, where *The Times* somewhat gullibly welcomed their 'aboriginal airs of the interior of Africa'. New groups formed, split and multiplied—including the Kentucky Minstrels, the Congo Minstrels, the Ethiopian Serenaders, the Sable Harmonizers, the Campbell Minstrels and, most famous of all, the Christy Minstrels, founded by Edwin P. Christy who claimed that he had invented the whole idea himself. And Christy employed the greatest popular composer of the nineteenth century, Stephen Foster.

Naturally, public reception of the Minstrels was not entirely rapturous. *Putnams Monthly* complained in 1854 that the Italian Opera had gone bankrupt while 'the Ethiopian opera has flourished like a green bay tree', and the previous year *Dwight's Journal of Music* remarked sourly that Minstrel melody was a disease that '*breaks out* every now and then, like a morbid irritation of the skin'.

The trouble was that the songs and dances were robust, tuneful, simple, catchy and comic, in their combination of Negro idiom and English folk-song elements a truly American folk-art. As the 'fifties and 'sixties progressed, however, a curious thing happened to the Minstrels. They were adopted by the middle class.

A new element, deriving from America's family troupes of singers, made its appearance: the moral—nostalgic—sentimental that easily slipped into the lugubrious. Minstrel bands became so sedate and doleful that burnt cork was synonymous with tears. Minstrel subject-matter now often departed from the plantation: 'Let Me Kiss Him for His Mother' (on page 290) is straight drawing-room sentimentalia owing nothing to Negro origin. The shows grew to include all kinds of specialty acts, sketches, stump speeches and short farces culminating in the 'walk around', the grand finale, with an opera burlesque or some other production number.

In Britain the Minstrels were nearly as much a craze as in the States. London's bourgeoisie took them to its heart almost from the first. They coincided with the anti-slavery sentiments encouraged by *Uncle Tom's Cabin* and also, paradoxically enough, with British admiration of the conservative South and its apparently idyllic plantations. 'A vagabond with a corked face and a banjo sings a little song,' remarked Thackeray the novelist, 'strikes a wild note, which sets the heart thrilling with happy pity.'

The Original Christy Minstrels, under the direction of the flamboyant George Washington Moore (nicknamed 'Pony' because of his predilection for driving mettlesome horseflesh), occupied St James's Hall where sedate audiences normally resorted to hear orchestral music and oratorio. They spawned travelling companies who still used the adjective 'Original', and were rivalled by such troupes as the Mohawk Minstrels, the Moore and Burgess Minstrels (run by 'Pony' Moore after leaving Christy) and the McNish, Johnson and Slaven's Refined Minstrels, all purveying similar improving, lachrymose songs and clean, if laborious, humour to which the strictest paterfamilias could take his children without a qualm. Minstrelsy spread to the streets. In *London Labour and the London Poor* of 1851–62, Henry Mayhew reported a street musician saying, 'Some niggers are Irish. There's Scotch niggers too. I don't know a Welsh one, but one of the street nigger-singers *is* a real black—an African.'

That was unusual, for real Negro performers were virtually unknown, even in America, until the 'seventies—when they had to use the same burnt cork as white actors for the standard make-up. By now the Minstrels were at their peak. Hundreds of companies made New York City and Philadelphia the great black-face centres, from which they toured the country—north of the Mason and Dixon line. The troupes, originally as few as four or six men in number, grew bigger and more glittering. Famous companies like Bryant's Minstrels found competitors in the Duprez and Benedict New Gigantic Minstrels, the Primrose and West Mammoth Minstrels and, to shouts of 'Forty! Count 'Em! Forty!', Colonel Jack Haverly and his Mastodon Minstrels. Finally, in the way that the cinema in desperation turned to wider screens and multiple soundtracks, elephantiasis set in, and in the 'eighties companies of a hundred or more were on tour. By trying to outdo each other in lavishness the Minstrel companies encompassed their own decline. The public grew tired; showbiz spectacle was no substitute for the lively directness and plain sentimentality that brought the Minstrels their enormous success. By the dawn of the twentieth century it was almost over. A few troupes struggled on and the black-face tradition reverted with individual 'coon' acts to vaudeville, circus and music-hall where, in effect, it had begun.

The full story of the Minstrels, despite some excellent studies of aspects of the movement, has yet to be written. It was an extremely curious phenomenon with strange facets—women, for instance, were as absent from the Minstrel platform as they had been from the Elizabethan stage. Imitation by the white man of Negro originals was not new, but why the 'Ethiopian business', as Stephen Foster called it, should have boomed so prodigiously still remains a matter for conjecture.

The Minstrel saga is over sixty years long, and not really finished yet. We must go back now to the early part of the nineteenth century to glance at another phenomenon, in its way equally important in the history of the parlour ballad. It was the itinerant musical entertainer, a man of unimpeachable moral intentions who had talents sufficiently varied to sing, accompany himself upon the pianoforte and perhaps a curious variety of other instruments. Charles Dibdin, the composer of 'Tom Bowling' and other nautical songs in praise of Jack Tar in the late eighteenth century, developed a style of one-man travelling entertainment that set the pattern for a hundred years. He eschewed stage costume—even singing his comic Negro songs without the aid of burnt cork—and gave the impression of a gentleman delighting his friends around the piano in a drawing-room. Henry Russell, an Englishman who spent his most productive years in the United States in the 'thirties, where he composed and sang such famous pieces as 'Woodman Spare That Tree' and 'A Life on the Ocean Wave' to words by American poets, made his fortune as an entertainer on both sides of the Atlantic. There were many of them and they all used a similar style, decorous and improving in their choice of material, but not averse to striking an awful attention in the audience with violently dramatic pieces, usually with showy piano accompaniments, about disasters at sea or heroism in battle on land.

It was in London that an actress and singer, Miss Priscilla Horton (1818–1895), hit upon the idea of bringing a number of such entertainers together in a stage show of great gentility with direct appeal to the careful paterfamilias. In 1855 she opened 'Miss P. Horton's Illustrative Gatherings' and filled the little St Martin's Hall in Longacre with enthusiastic middle-class audiences who would normally never be seen near a theatre. She married Thomas German Reed (1817–1888), who accompanied her upon the piano or harmonium, and occasionally donned grease-paint as an actor. 'Mr and Mrs German Reed's Entertainments' at the Gallery of Illustration in Regent Street were a godsend to London's bourgeoisie, which did not want to be shocked or embarrassed when it took its children for an evening's pleasure. There was not much chance, for example, of Mrs German Reed's turning an impressionable young man's head, for she was respectability personified and of somewhat Wagnerian dimensions. Of similar corpulence was her leading entertainer, the massive and genial Corney Grain, an ex-barrister, a master of mild satire who could reduce an audience to tears of genteel hilarity. The German Reeds were true musicians, and they could unbend. We owe them a great debt, for among the operettas that they introduced into their programme was *Cox and Box*, a lively little musical farce with text by F. C. Burnand that introduced the young Arthur Sullivan to comic opera. He and W. S. Gilbert were to create the great series of Savoy Operas that perpetuated the German Reeds' note of inoffensive gaiety.

Needless to say, with the German Reeds presenting stage shows, the Minstrels singing their lugubrious ballads and the entertainers constantly on tour, there was much overlap between them. With the rise of music-hall the edges became even more blurred, and performers moved happily from one medium to another. The singer and comedian, George Grossmith, senior, writer of 'See Me Dance the Polka', was a leading figure in Gilbert and Sullivan, an entertainer respectable enough to delight Queen Victoria, and he did not disdain playing the music-halls. Even an artiste like Albert Chevalier, the master of Cockney ballads on the halls, singer and composer of such classics as 'My Old Dutch' and 'Knocked 'Em in the Old Kent Road', gave 'Chevalier Recitals' at the Queen's Hall in the 'nineties to the kind of audience who never entered the music-hall. Perhaps it was the maudlin sentimentality of his material that provided the necessary touch of respectability.

The entertainers introduced very many songs that reached the parlour, but they were not the only singers to do so. The leading exponents of opera and oratorio included high-class ballads in their recital programmes throughout the century and, indeed, were responsible for the introduction of the royalty system in Britain. Serious music may have been their first love, but it was so profitable to sing for music publishers at ballad concerts from the late 'sixties onwards that many of the country's greatest voices achieved fame principally for their renderings of the latest successes from Boosey or Chappell. Such important vocalists as the tenor Sims Reeves, the baritone Sir Charles Santley, the soprano Madame Antoinette Sterling and the contralto Madame Sainton-Dolby introduced the latest hits precisely as disc jockeys and pop groups do today. Even if they were not part of the ballad concert circle, the great international singers of the day, Jenny Lind, Adelina Patti and their like, sang 'Home, Sweet Home' and other affecting ballads as the high spots of their concerts.

The first real ballad concert dates from 1867. It was the outcome of a chat between Madame Sainton-Dolby and the music publisher John Boosey. The venue was the St James's Hall in London, the home of the Saturday and Monday Popular Concerts of orchestral and chamber music, and Boosey's enterprise was soon copied by his rivals, the Chappell family and other publishers such as Cramer and Enoch. Practically all the famous names in British singing appeared at these affairs. Antoinette Sterling was perhaps the greatest ballad singer of them all; she introduced such parlour masterpieces as 'The Lost Chord' (on page 234) and sang at every one of Boosey's ballad concerts for twenty consecutive seasons. The concerts were copied all over the British Isles, and particularly at seaside resorts and spas where the polite world sought good health and good company. In America, a concert would be announced, as in England, under some such euphonious title as 'A Grand Morning Concert' or 'A Select Soirée Musicale'. Sir Frederic Cowen, a British composer of great réclame, quoted in his autobiography verses by one of his lyric writers, Robert Francillon. Here is a stanza:

> When I survey the glorious scene
>   A Ballad Concert shows—
> The singer dressed in pink and green,
>   The audience all in rows—
> To write a song I burn to try,
>   A song—oh, pride to tell!
> For Boosey's customers to buy,
>   And Boosey's self to sell.

Of course, what Boosey sold to Boosey's customers was sheet music, in quantities that almost rival those of pop records now. Most of the British songs in this collection from the 'seventies onwards were products of 'the ballad boom', and they first thrilled the ears of the multitude from the stages of London's concert halls. At first a programme would consist entirely of solos with a few instrumental pieces interpolated for variety. Later, when ballad concerts were flagging in popular favour, orchestral pieces of the lighter variety bolstered the entertainment. The ballad, however, was always the main attraction, and its promotion by the royalty system was the foundation of the whole business.

The system was a simple one. The composer and lyricist of a song might receive an outright fee, often a very modest one, or a small royalty upon public performances, but it was the singer who was paid munificent sums by music publishers to introduce the song and, if it met general acclaim, to maintain it in his repertoire. John Boosey complained in his autobiography of what seemed to him an abuse of the royalty arrangement, extending fees beyond the select group of the most celebrated vocalists:

> In the old days the leading singers also received a royalty for a term of years upon all new songs introduced by them. Antoinette Sterling, for instance, would have a royalty on 'The Lost Chord' of Sullivan's, 'The Better Land' of Cowen's, 'Darby and Joan' and 'Love's Old Sweet Song', both by Molloy. After introduction by a big singer, all the smaller singers, according to their voices, would take up those same ballads. One publisher made himself unpopular by paying royalties to minor singers and others were compelled to follow suit.

Vocalists' names were prominent on nearly all the sheet music of the period, and they were often in much larger type than the names of composer or poet. The latters' names were sometimes omitted altogether. The size of fees a leading singer could command depended, of course, upon his prominence. They could be startlingly high; Edward Lloyd, the tenor, reported in an interview in the *Musical Times* in 1899 that he thought the most popular song in his repertoire was 'The Holy City' by Stephen Adams: 'It sells at the rate of 50,000 copies per annum. In Montreal I was engaged to sing four times in one month at a fee of 250 guineas each concert, *on condition* that I sang "The Holy City" on each occasion.' Needless to say, many serious commentators upon music saw the royalty system as having a most deleterious effect upon the literary and musical standards of songs, and it certainly resulted in a vast flood of ballads, only a small proportion of which caught the popular fancy and even fewer of which had much merit. Singers generally had no qualms about providing musical fare appealing to the tastes of their audiences; indeed, their own tastes were often very similar. Adelina Patti was subjected to frequent critical disapproval on account of her limited repertoire and her addiction to 'Home, Sweet Home' and 'Comin' through the Rye'. Dame Nellie Melba spent much energy in the 'twenties of this century denying that she had ever given a certain piece of well-meaning advice to Dame Clara Butt, about to tour Australia. 'Sing 'em muck,' she is supposed to have said, 'it's all they can understand.'

If middle-class music was the recipient of critical scorn, how much more of a target was that emanating from the music-hall. Today, when distinguished literary men and sober theatrical historians hymn the gaiety, vigour and irreverence of music-hall, one must remember that very few of their counterparts eighty years ago would ever have admitted to have passed through those glittering if grubby portals. In the new twentieth century the halls became more acceptable, but in Victoria's reign only the working class and the emancipated—and therefore socially suspect—found great delight there. Rudyard Kipling and Max Beerbohm were among the writers who were enthusiastic visitors, and Walter Sickert and John Pennell among the painters. In the 'sixties the Reverend Haweis rather surprisingly commended the penny gaffs, forerunners in part of true music-hall, because they were 'coarse . . . but on the whole moral and contrasting most favourably with anything of the kind in France'. Some male members of the aristocracy, given to a freedom of taste denied to those a few rungs below them on the social ladder, found the halls much to their tastes, and leading artistes like Dan Leno were often to be found performing in the best drawing-rooms, having arrived there, one imagines, by the tradesmen's entrance. Leno received royal approval from the Prince of Wales, and when the latter ascended the throne was able to dub himself 'The King's Jester'.

But this approval of music-hall was exceptional. The official middle-class attitude was one of stern disapproval—when the disreputable phenomenon was noticed at all. 'Insane trash,' commented the *Musical Times* in 1868; 'drivel for the dregs', thundered an Edwardian journalist, and a late-Victorian jurist remarked portentously, 'If music-halls were closed a great service would be done to the State, for they are the bane of modern London, corrupting and debasing youth, and creating a distaste for all intellectual pastimes.' There is little doubt that the young bloods of Kensington, Hampstead or Balham and Peckham, scions of sober suburban homes, were sowing their wild oats to the usual disapproval of their elders.

The middle-aged bourgeoisie, then, stayed away, in the same manner as the primmer merchants of New York City avoided the offering of vaudeville on Broadway. Only once a year in London, towards the end of Victoria's reign would the more liberal-minded members of the middle class be seen at the halls: they took their children to the pantomime, in which the principal roles were played by music-hall favourites. Somehow, the tinsel and bad puns of the traditional British Christmas show transcended in respectable eyes the vulgarity of the theatres in which it was staged.

The sentimental ballads of the music-hall, and there were many of them, can easily be distinguished from the drawing-room variety: a certain over-emphasis in provoking the starting tear and reliance upon blatantly stock situations indicate a more plebeian origin. None the less, judging by the sheet-music sales, many of them had great currency in the parlour as well as on the boards. A few, 'That is Love', 'The Ship I Love', 'Shall I be an Angel, Daddy?' and 'The Miner's Dream of Home', are included in this volume, although, sadly, the great, vigorous body of broad, comic music-hall melody has to be omitted.

Where America is concerned, it is more difficult to exclude the sentimental productions of late nineteenth-century vaudeville and variety. These songs, the harvest of the lusty young Tin Pan Alley, met with great favour in suburban parlours, usually far less strait-laced about matters of social degree than their British equivalents. Vaudeville (the name dates from the 'eighties) was, all the same, not for the more decorous public. The less sedate flocked to '444 Broadway' and other variety theatres to see acrobats, musical turns, juggling and topical and sentimental songs. Women generally stayed away, but as the years went by the institution gradually became more respectable. Despite the constant traffic of lyrics and tunes back and forth across the Atlantic, apart from some transplanted ventures there was no exact parallel to the British music-hall in New York or other American cities—although, in contrast, music-hall did emigrate very successfully to Australia.

There was in the States, however, in addition to vaudeville a splendid and unique institution that gave birth to an annual feast of melody: the shows of Harrigan and Hart. Their mixture of mirth and tenderness, mostly based on Irish themes, was as strictly American as music-hall was firmly British, and by the end of the century their influence had produced the bouncing new baby of musical comedy that grew rapidly to maturity in both countries. As a tribute to Harrigan and Hart, one of their most famous songs, 'Maggie Murphy's Home' is printed on page 174.

Tin Pan Alley, another purely American institution, was a commercial brotherhood of New York lyricists and composers who, while exploiting the sentimental ballad to its utmost, managed, in fact, to help destroy it by ridicule. Certain hard-living, hard-drinking and hard-bitten denizens of Tin Pan Alley had intentions that were open to question. While some, like Paul Dresser ('The Banks of the Wabash', 'The Blue and the Gray' and 'The Pardon Came Too Late', which appears on page 322), composer brother (although he spelled his name differently) of the novelist Theodore Dreiser, were utterly sincere and serious, there is little doubt that Monroe H. Rosenfeld ('Johnnie, Get Your Hair Cut', 'With All Her Faults I Love Her Still', 'Take Back Your Gold') wrote a number of tear-provoking ballads with something less than seriousness, and his contemporary Edward B. Marks ('The Little Lost Child', 'Mother was a Lady') in candid moments admitted as much about his own pieces. A number of their songs can be seen as deliberate satires upon the saccharine effusions that earned them their daily liquor. Charles K. Harris ('After the Ball', 'Break the News to Mother') wrote a particularly choice example that was sung by Marie Dressler, 'Heaven Will Protect the Working Girl':

> Stand back, villain, go your way! here I will no longer stay,
> Although you were a marquis or an earl;
> You may tempt the upper classes with your villainous demitasses,
> But Heaven will protect the working girl.

Most of the Alley's output, however, was nominally straight-faced, although by twisting the screw of sentimentality to the uttermost the song writers of the 'nineties were in danger of passing from pathos into bathos. They represent the parlour ballad run to seed, and it strains one's credulity today that they were ever taken seriously—as they certainly were.

16

IV

If the subject-matter of parlour songs is common to that of most periods—love, death, childhood, the home, patriotic exhortation, the sea and so on—this treatment does give a revealing glimpse of how the Victorians felt about those basic themes. There were several degrees of love, for instance. Indeed, affection between male and female was seen to be of an inferior quality to the noble devotion of man for his maker, of a mother to her baby or one comrade for another in adversity. Felix McGlennon's 'That is Love' (on page 64) is a primer for those who may have fallen into such a common error:

> 'Tis not the love, the love for a beauteous face,
> 'Tis not the love that Time's ravages soon will chase;
> 'Tis not the love from brightly sparkling eyes,
> No! 'tis the love sent from Paradise.

It would have been a bold lover who would have quarrelled with that admonishment. Profane love in this volume is singularly pure, too. It has little to do with the grosser attributes of procreation. However wholehearted these songs they seldom mention physical qualities of the adored situated lower than the chin (although the extremities of the limbs may be permitted sugared compliments) and never touch upon the reason for the whole elaborate ritual. They are, practically all of them, rosy-tinted evasions. Many girls, nurtured on drawing-room ballads, apparently went to the altar expecting in married life no more alarming contact with their husbands than the tickle of a manly whisker. It is surprising, therefore, that so many middle-class marriages were happy as well as fecund.

If parlour love sidestepped the vital issues, how much more so did ballads of action. The reek of powder, the blast of shot and shell, blood and sweat are not to be found soiling the drawing-room drapes. Nor does the numbing blast of the gale, the spindrift of the ocean's swell lash the potted ferns or set the bobbles swaying along the mantel-shelf too violently. Battle here is more a matter of heroic attitudes, and soldiers bleed sawdust. The sea's fury roars with a distinctly theatrical note, too. Songs of the deep generally perpetuate myth, whether of noble self-sacrifice in shipwreck or of the sterling qualities of that archetypal character the jolly Jack Tar. The reasons for this are not far to find, but it is fascinating to see how, during the American Civil War, songs reflected the growing gap between death in battle as a romantic prospect and death in battle as an appalling fact. But all the same, the ballads of that period have an elegiac quality, and the view of conflict is that of the bereaved safely by the fireside. The result is genuine grief indulged, even exploited, to an extent that later generations find morbid. 'The Vacant Chair' (on page 318), 'Dear Mother, I've Come Home to Die' (on page 314), both from the early 1860s, are among the examples in this volume.

Nevertheless, we should not adopt too smug an attitude. Television brings the full immediate pornography of violence into our homes; the Victorians had only bloodless steel engravings and the suitably edited tales of survivors upon which to base their feelings.

Death stalks the pages of this collection, as it must any anthology of Victorian popular art. Deathbed scenes punctuate novels, plays, songs and verse in infinite variation. Soldiers' breasts expand to meet the oncoming ball, babies expire in their cots, mothers freeze in snowstorms, fathers are crushed beneath runaway locomotives (having saved a wandering toddler in the process) and grandmothers fall gently asleep in old armchairs. Death was then even more obviously omnipresent in life than now, of course.

The death-rate from disease, inexpert medical care and poverty was very high by our standards, and as the middle class donned the sober garb of gentility they also strove to improve death. The sting of reality was removed by romanticising it. And, in some curious way, sentimentalised death became an international drug: several generations found in it satisfaction, enjoyment and harmless entertainment. Maybe in a hundred years' time anthologists will be commenting upon the curious preoccupation idealised sex had for the twentieth century, sex as closely related to the less glamorous facts as Victorian death to the infinitely less genteel reality.

Death was closely rivalled as a topic for lyrics by home. A deep longing for security, for both the emotional and physical comforts of the family fireside are a constant theme throughout the nineteenth century. For it was far from a settled period, pre-eminently the Age of Emigration. Millions who had scarcely stirred for centuries more than a few miles from their ancestral acres travelled to seek new lives in grimy factory towns or in the Promised Lands of the United States, Canada, Australia or South Africa. The population of Ireland dropped some four millions between 1841 and 1901.

It is not surprising, therefore, that many songs of travel, exile and yearning for home should be Irish in character, nor that the bulk of them should be American. As families divided and scattered, the stronger was the need to maintain emotional bonds. There is nothing strange in the fact that the song that has almost certainly been sung more times than any other from this period, 'Home! Sweet Home!', should have been written by a man who never had a home of his own and was condemned by fate to wander all his life. For all its apparent mawkishness and poverty of melody it encapsulates the most powerful yearning and heartbreak.

And for 'home' in many of these songs read 'mother', for she is hymned to an inordinate extent. The great all-American mom dates from these years. In the absence of father, who was likely to be away flinging the nation's Western frontier even further, many families became matriarchies. Well-loved objects also act their roles as symbols of home. Woodmen are urged to spare that tree, and grandfathers' clocks, old armchairs, old oaken buckets, old spinning-wheels and old rustic bridges by the mill are all pressed into service as *aide-mémoires* for the exile. The very adjective 'old' suggests security and permanence.

Naturally, romance casts a rosy aura overall. The old oaken bucket, as a latterday parodist pointed out, bred hosts of malignant bacilli and would have been condemned by the public health authorities. Travel also had its magical aspects: we have in this volume a few examples of Victorian Araby, that never-never land that existed only in the pages of Sir Richard Burton, the graceful cynicisms of Omar Kayyám, countless songs and more recently in the films of Rudolf Valentino.

Nowhere, however, does romance flourish so luxuriantly as in songs about children. Nowhere does the cliché bloom so fragrantly. In this period of large families and high infant mortality, nearly everybody must have followed a small coffin at some time or other to the graveyard. At such moments, and with the ever-present fear of such sad events recurring, the cliché was the least upsetting form of communication: by generalising grief the Victorians could deal with their own particular sorrows. With their innocence and trust, children were ideal material, too, from which to point morals. Songs of babes and striplings tend therefore to be particularly improving in their sentiments. In passing on to heaven, doomed infants point out to their sorrowing relatives—or even to casual passers-by—the road to a new and better life.

Improvement, especially self-improvement, was an unassailable article of the nine-teenth-century moral creed. As already mentioned, song was pressed into service for the active propagation of good. Armed only with hymn-books, pianofortes, pedestrian organs and their all-conquering religious zeal, the middle classes of Britain and America stormed into the moral conflict. The bulk of nineteenth-century moral balladry, however, is somewhat gentler, falling into the category of fine sentiments, and these songs were the progenitors of the art ballads that were to have such a following in the first part of the twentieth century. This volume contains several famous specimens; they still sound remarkably well today. To hear the archetypal parlour song, Sir Arthur Sullivan's 'The Lost Chord', sympathetically performed with harmonium accompaniment, is to appreciate almost everything the Victorians admired in such music. Lyric, sentiment, tune and harmony: all are utterly and uniquely of the period.

The themes in this collection mingle and intertwine to an astonishing degree. Dying children populate temperance ballads, love songs have a strong element of religiosity, amid the smoke of battle soldiers spare a thought for home. The minstrel songs, especially, draw their subjects from far and wide, however localised the romanticised plantation setting. These ballads are, together, a window into the Victorian middle-class soul.

V

Whatever their origin, parlour ballads conform to an instantly recognisable musical as well as literary style. To begin with, they were absolutely singable, usually easy to read, easy to memorise and in tune with the ideas expressed in their lyrics. There is little to intrigue us intellectually, but if we are prepared to approach these songs with understanding and appreciation of their *raison d'être*, not solemnly yet without facetiousness, they have much to offer. Their melodic sentiments, like their textual sentiments, are out of date, but not for that reason invalid. Bach's melodic sentiments were out of date until Mendelssohn and Barnby, among others, discovered their qualities to a new generation. They are as valid now, within their own limitations, as they were in the 1720s. So, if the comparison may be allowed, is the Victorian ballad as valid as it has ever been. Taste has dated it, and taste is notoriously fickle. Anyone who doubts it should recall that at the top of the British pops not long ago was Rolf Harris's version of 'Two Little Boys', an ultra-sentimental ballad with origins in the American Civil War, a piece of pure Victoriana.

For the most part, these songs use, to our eyes, a fairly unsophisticated harmonic language. We have lost the ability to fear the diminished seventh or to thrill to an arpeggio, for we have broken free from most Victorian musical conventions. In order to appreciate parlour ballads to the full we need to approach them with a degree of ingenuousness so far as the harmonic language is concerned. We must be faintly reassured and not bored by modulations to the dominant and sub-dominant, and other modulations should be exciting if not a little unsettling. Above all we should be able to revel in the absolute security of the perfect cadence and the home key.

As with the music, nineteenth-century styles of vocalisation are very different to those of the late twentieth. One has only to listen to early recordings to meet a manner of singing totally at variance with present standards of acceptability. Our relatively advanced musicological knowledge has now taught us that ours is not the only correct way of singing.

Nowadays we have little time for the chest voice of Clara Butt, however much she delighted her admirers seventy years ago by her invitation to 'Put your head on my shoulder, Daddy'. We have little time for the portamento that characterised some of Adelina Patti's most famous interpretations. Nevertheless, we should recognise that for the Victorians, in opera house, on concert platform and at home, these two devices were indispensable for the proper enjoyment of vocal music. There was, moreover, the vibrato. Whatever later critics have said, a Victorian voice without a vibrato, and a fairly wide one at that, was like a kiss without a moustache. In fact, it was only the very widest of vibrato, taking in a good semitone on either side of the note, that was liable to be frowned upon by the purist at a concert. If that was the case in public performance, one can only hazard what excesses made the glassware ring in the privacy of the parlour.

For a full appreciation of drawing-room songs today, we should seek to restore some of these ancillaries of performance, so long as over-indulgence does not make them unacceptably ridiculous to our ears.

It is not only the singer who can recapture some, at least, of the style of Victorian renditions. The pianist, too, can enhance the charm of his accompaniment by his receptiveness and sensitiveness to past musical manners. Nineteenth-century domestic piano music was designed to give the maximum of showiness with the minimum of technique. Many melodies are based upon a harmonic scheme of about three chords and include passages of brilliant arpeggiated figures, so the capabilities of the pianist were generally not greatly taxed by most song accompaniments. A secure grounding in Mrs Curwen's *Pianoforte Method* and a reasonable familiarity with the stave qualified any player, provided that he was reasonably musical, to accompany a singer through a parlour ballad. Such difficulties that did arise would have been easily overcome by assiduous scale practice and a little time, a commodity sadly lacking today. For the present-day pianist, as for the singer, the important thing to aim for is sincerity and intelligence of statement.

In performing Victorian songs, we, like our forbears, should use as much light and shade as possible, revel in the showy passages and linger to wring a tear from the pathetic. We have to tread the delicate and indeed perilous line between too great a seriousness and the temptation to guy the original. Of course, many ballads in this collection are faintly ridiculous, to say the least; even these can still be enjoyed enormously if performers and audience are properly ambivalent in their attitude. One can still appreciate a piece for its very real qualities while realising that those qualities, and other features of the song, raise a smile today. The Balfe setting of 'Excelsior!', extravagant and operatic, demands and repays a full-blooded interpretation; it is still genuinely exciting and yet, because of its overstatement, is *also* genuinely hilarious. It is, in fact, the supreme example of good bad music. Finally, we must recognise that some ballads, such as 'My Old Kentucky Home' and 'I'll Sing Thee Songs of Araby', transcend all the restrictions of style and period; they are, quite simply, marvellous songs.

VI

Any anthology must inevitably exclude infinitely more than it can admit into its pages. This one is no exception, and any reader with even a superficial knowledge of nineteenth-century songs will be disappointed because particular favourites have been cold-shouldered. Such is the wide variety of Victorian vocal music, indeed, that whole areas have had to be omitted. The basis for selection has been simply that the songs chosen should be primarily Gems adopted by British and American families for performance in the parlour and drawing-room during the reign of Queen Victoria. They have been selected, too, to give performer and auditor pleasure today, and that, perhaps, after the qualification already mentioned, is the single most important reason for the presence of a song here. So far as is possible, the book includes representatives of all the important types of song—sentimental, descriptive, pathetic and proselytising—on the main themes and preoccupations of the time—love, death, childhood, home, social and moral improvement—from the principal sources of balladry—opera, ballad concerts, family troupes, the Minstrels, music-hall—and of the century's favourite composers from Henry Bishop and Henry Russell to Arthur Sullivan and Ethelbert Nevin.

Quite a number of the ballads collected here come from the first forty years of the century—'The Last Rose of Summer', one of Moore's *Irish Melodies*, for instance—for until the 'ballad boom' of the 'seventies and Tin Pan Alley of the 'nineties, seasonal favourites that burst into flower and withered in months were exceptional and songs could have an active life in the parlour of sixty years or more. The most notable omission from this volume, as already mentioned, is the mighty body of comic songs from music-hall and vaudeville. Although the more liberal parlour would delight in them, rather, as Colin McInnes suggests in *Sweet Saturday Night*, as the middle class now enjoys pop records, they belong to the working class and must reluctantly be excluded. The exceptions printed here are certain sentimental ballads that had great sheet-music sales and while they owe their immediate origin to the music-hall are attached in spirit and greatest popularity to the parlour.

Another group excluded, unfairly perhaps, from this pantheon are songs from the operettas of Gilbert and Sullivan. They had immense currency in the drawing-room; 'A Wandering Minstrel I', 'Take a Pair of Sparkling Eyes' and dozens of others made the palm fronds tremble in myriad homes from the 'seventies onwards, but they are easily to be found by present-day afficionados and for that reason are not included here. Similarly, a number of highly popular Victorian songs, such as 'Clementine' and 'Sweet Adeline', have made room for equally enjoyable but less accessible ballads.

Like the comic music-hall songs, student songs are missing because they were not parlour fare. Also absent are national airs and folk songs unless they were heavily adapted and sterilised for polite audiences, like 'The Last Rose of Summer'.

A warning about the texts of the lyrics in this collection is necessary. Where previously published verses have been set to music, as is the case with such songs as 'Excelsior!', 'Come into the Garden, Maud', 'Ben Bolt' and 'Rock Me to Sleep, Mother', the text of the ballad is frequently different from the original poem. Punctuation inevitably suffers a change, but some lyrics are travesties of their originals—'Ben Bolt' is a painful example—and others make near-nonsense of certain lines—Balfe was particularly cavalier in his treatment of 'Come into the Garden, Maud'.

If some of the texts of the songs are doubtful, the same may be said of their recorded histories. There have been many volumes of stories of famous songs published from the late nineteenth century until quite recently, and the accretion of anecdote has resulted in the origins of several songs being hidden under layers of romantic nonsense. Some volumes of slapdash scholarship, such as S. J. Adair Fitzgerald's *Stories of Famous Songs*, 1898, are extremely confusing—if disarmingly entertaining—and it is very possible that some of the details in the notes to the songs in this anthology are open to question. This editor would welcome correction where necessary.

VII

Finally, I should like to return briefly to a couple of points made earlier in this Introduction. It was D. B. Wyndham Lewis and Charles Lee, in their classic anthology,

The Stuffed Owl, who first formally stated the concept of good bad verse. A very few of the ballads in this collection are good by any standards; a handful are splendidly, joyously bad, masterpieces in the art of sinking. Most of them, however, are flawed to some extent by hackneyed or at least out-of-date sentiments in the poetry or by clumsy or ingenuous musicianship, by lack of inspiration or simple wrong-headedness. Because they can all still be enjoyed, despite all their defects, they fall into that category, which is not the same as the mediocre, of good bad art.

Good music can suffer and survive somewhat inadequate performance. It is not the case with good bad music which, in unsympathetic hands, is unbearable. Earlier, it has been suggested that these pieces be performed with enthusiasm, coupled with restraint. Perhaps for the most complete enjoyment singer and accompanist should pay heed to the attitude of one of the greatest of all nineteenth-century interpreters of the ballad, Madame Antoinette Sterling. The prolific lyricist, Fred E. Weatherly, wrote of her in his autobiography: '. . . I was delighted to write for a singer who, as was the case with her, would sing no song, even if the music suited her vocally, unless she believed in the words and felt them and could sing them as though they were her own.' Today we do not, with Sterling, have to believe heart and soul in every word as we perform these songs, but we can certainly render them as if we did, with affection tempered by understanding. It is more than just acting a part, it is becoming for a while a Victorian, with a Victorian's vigour, sincerity and moral fervour: instead of wearing fancy dress to assume period costume. One cannot but quote Antoinette Sterling again, writing of her approach to 'The Three Fishers' by The Reverend Charles Kingsley, set by John Hullah: 'Although I had never been to sea in a storm, and had never even seen fishermen, I somehow understood that song of "The Three Fishers" by instinct.' That sentence sums up both the whole feeling of parlour balladry and how it may be presented today.

M. R. T.

Hearts & Flowers

or, Songs of Love

My Pretty Jane

(The Bloom is on the Rye)

Written by Edward Fitzball   Composed by Sir Henry Bishop

Andantino espressione, non troppo lento

dolce sostenuto

1. My pret – ty Jane! my pret-ty Jane!_____ Ah! ne-ver ne-ver look so shy, But meet me, meet me in the Ev' – ning, While the bloom is_ on_ the

My Pretty Jane

Rye._____ The Spring is wan-ing fast, my Love, The corn__ is in__ the

ear. The Sum-mer nights are com-ing. Love, The moon shines bright and__

clear; Then pret-ty Jane, my dear - est Jane, Ah! nev -er look so

shy,__ But meet me, meet me in the Ev' - ning, While the bloom is on__ the

Rye._____

25

My Pretty Jane

1. My pretty Jane! my pretty Jane!
   Ah! never look so shy,
But meet me, meet me in the Ev'ning,
   While the bloom is on the Rye.
The Spring is waning fast, my Love
   The corn is in the ear,
The Summer nights are coming, Love,
   The moon shines bright and clear;
Then pretty Jane, my dearest Jane,
   Ah! never look so shy,
But meet me, meet me in the Ev'ning,
   While the bloom is on the Rye.

2. But **name** the day, the wedding day,
   And I will buy the ring.
The Lads and Maids in favours white,
   And village bells shall ring.
The Spring is waning fast, my Love,
   The corn is in the ear,
The Summer nights are coming, Love,
   The moon shines bright and clear;
Then pretty Jane, my dearest Jane,
   Ah! never look so shy,
But meet me, meet me in the Ev'ning,
   While the bloom is on the Rye.

'My Pretty Jane' had a great celebrity all through the century, linked as it was with the name of the famous tenor, Sims Reeves, who used it almost as a signature tune. It had originally been written by Edward Fitzball, when a youth, to hymn the charms of a pretty farmer's daughter who lived near his home at Burwell, near Newmarket in Suffolk. One summer's day, after seeing Jane peep coyly at him through her window, Fitzball sat down on a stile and wrote the lyric in less than ten minutes. The girl, it is said, died later of consumption, but the poet treasured the portrait he had painted of her for long afterwards. Years after writing the song, Fitzball was providing lyrics for the management of Vauxhall pleasure gardens; he found it and gave it to Henry Bishop to set. When visiting Bishop, Fitzball discovered the song, which Bishop had composed and discarded, in the latter's wastepaper-basket whence the poet retrieved it. The same night it was sung to an enormous furore. It was first published as 'The Bloom is on the Rye'.

Sensitive auditors will note the false rhyme of 'ring' and 'ring' in the second stanza. Fitzball altered it later, when he published a volume of poems, to:

> Oh, name the day, the wedding day,
>   And I will buy the ring;
> The bells shall peal love's roundelay,
>   And village maids shall sing.

Fitzball (1792–1873) was born plain Ball: he acquired the prefix, which suggests aristocratic illegitimacy, to chime more harmoniously with his ambitions. He tried to set up a printing office in Norwich, but found his true avocation to lie in writing the more extravagant kind of melodrama for London theatres. Indeed, the typical Jack Tar nautical drama is credited as his invention; he had, of course, borrowed the character from Charles Dibdin. He was librettist for all of Balfe's early operas as well as Wallace's *Maritana* and other musical dramas. Despite the lurid nature of the material that he provided in such profusion, Fitzball was a quiet, sentimental little man. 'Gentle Fitzball' was his nickname, and although of somewhat unprepossessing aspect, for he had a huge nose of strange shape, he thought he was irresistible to women. This daunting exterior was not helped by the guttural tones of his voice which sounded almost like a speech impediment. He was so much of a hack writer that Britain's august *Dictionary of National Biography* could not bring itself to notice him.

Sir Henry Bishop, although a noted reprobate, was at least respectable enough to be knighted. A note on his career appears on page 143.

She Wore a Wreath of Roses

Written by THOMAS HAYNES BAYLY

Composed by JOSEPH P. KNIGHT

1. She wore a wreath of ros - es, The night that first we met; Her
2. A wreath of or - ange blos - soms When next we met she wore; Th' ex -

love - ly face was smil - ing Be - neath her curls of jet; Her
- pres - sion of her fea - tures Was more thoughtful than be - fore; And

27

foot-step had the light-ness, Her voice the joy-ous tone, The
stand-ing by her side was one, Who strove, and not in vain, To

to-kens of a youth-ful heart, Where sor-row is un-known. I
soothe her leav-ing that dear home, She ne'er might view a-gain. I

saw her but a mo-ment, Yet me-thinks I see her now, With the
saw her but a mo-ment, Yet me-thinks I see her now, With the

wreath of sum-mer flow-ers, Up-on her snow-y brow.
wreath of or-ange blos-soms Up-on her snow-y brow.

D.S.

D.S.

mf

p

3. And once a-gain I see that brow. No brid-al wreath was there, The

wi-dow's som-bre cap con-ceals Her once lux-ur-iant hair; She

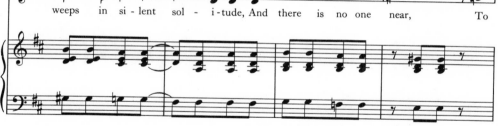

weeps in si-lent sol - i-tude, And there is no one near, To

press her hand with-in his own, And wipe a-way — the tear. I

saw her brok - en-heart-ed, Yet me-thinks I see her now, — In the

pride of youth and — beau-ty, With a gar - land on her brow.

She Wore a Wreath of Roses

1. She wore a wreath of roses,
    The night that first we met;
  Her lovely face was smiling
    Beneath her curls of jet;
  Her footstep had the lightness,
    Her voice the joyous tone,
  The tokens of a youthful heart,
    Where sorrow is unknown.
  I saw her but a moment,
    Yet methinks I see her now,
  With the wreath of summer flowers,
    Upon her snowy brow.

2. A wreath of orange blossoms
    When next we met she wore;
  Th'expression of her features
    Was more thoughtful than before;
  And standing by her side was one,
    Who strove, and not in vain,
  To soothe her leaving that dear home,
    She ne'er might view again.
  I saw her but a moment,
    Yet methinks I see her now,
  With the wreath of orange blossoms
    Upon her snowy brow.

3. And once again I see that brow,
    No bridal wreath was there,
  The widow's sombre cap conceals
    Her once luxuriant hair;
  She weeps in silent solitude,
    And there is no one near,
  To press her hand within his own,
    And wipe away the tear.
  I saw her broken-hearted,
    Yet methinks I see her now,
  In the pride of youth and beauty,
    With a garland on her brow.

This song was famous enough to be frequently parodied, possibly because the lyric lends itself to some very coy *double entendre*. The musical setting, however, is excellent.

The society poet, Thomas Haynes Bayly (1797–1829), makes his delicate appearance twice in this volume: 'The Soldier's Tear' is also his. If no great literary figure, and one that invited, and received, much ridicule, Bayly deserves more than the ignominious obscurity in which he now rests—if only as a significant figure of his time. Educated at Winchester and Oxford, he was very conscious of his noble connections. Nevertheless, lack of money and unlucky investments forced him to sing for his supper, and he turned out great quantities of graceful verse, songs and dramatic pieces. An American commentator of the 'nineties, Henry Frederic Reddall, took unkind delight in swatting this poetical butterfly in remarking that he had

considerable wit and humour, but his sentiment was too often mere sentimentalism, his love lackadaisical, and his melancholy very genteel and effeminate—wearing white gloves and wiping its eyes, in which there were no tears, with a highly perfumed cambric pocket-handkerchief—a very Mantalini of the art of poetastry.

Joseph Philip Knight (1812–1887) was a singer, composer and, eventually, Church of England clergyman in the parish of St Agnes in the Scilly Isles. He published over two hundred melodious songs, none of which the parlour vocalist or pianist would find too ambitious, under his own name and that of 'Philip Mortimer'. He spent a year in America, teaching music for a while at a school run by the educator Mrs Emma Willard, and wrote the music for her poem, 'Rock'd in the Cradle of the Deep'.

The Dream

(from *The Bohemian Girl*)

Written by ALFRED BUNN

Composed by M. W. BALFE

dreamt that I dwelt— in mar - ble halls, With vas -sals and

The Dream

serfs at my side,———— And of all who as - sem - bled with - in———— those walls That I was the hope and the pride.———— I had rich - es too great——to count——could boast Of a high—— an - ces - tral name.———— But I al - so

The Dream

1. I dreamt that I dwelt in marble halls,
   With vassals and serfs at my side,
   And of all those assembled within those walls
   That I was the hope and the pride.
   I had riches too great to count—could boast
   Of a high ancestral name.
   But I also dreamt; which pleas'd me most,
   That you loved me still the same.

2. I dreamt that suitors sought my hand;
   That knights, upon bended knee,
   And with vows that no maiden heart could withstand,
   They pledged their faith to me.
   And I dreamt that one of that noble host
   Came forth my hand to claim;
   But I also dreamt; which charm'd me most,
   That you loved me still the same.

The Bohemian Girl of 1843 was a gallant attempt to rival the Italian Opera in London. It had all the trappings of popular success: an heiress kidnapped, an aristocrat exiled, a gipsy setting, a recognition scene and sundry melodramatic etceteras. It created a rage for gipsy garb, the composer was awarded the Légion d'Honneur after the Paris production, and in Germany the opera delighted multitudes as *La Zingara*. Alfred Bunn and M. W. Balfe had co-operated before with *The Siege of Rochelle*, which Bunn produced and for which Edward Fitzball provided the libretto, and again with *The Maid of Artois*. After the fantastic brouhaha made by *The Bohemian Girl*—it contained several other celebrated arias, among them 'The Heart Bowed Down'—Bunn tried to repeat his success. *Maritana*, with music by Vincent Wallace, was also rapturously received on both sides of the Atlantic. Balfe went on to compose other operas, but nothing recreated the same furore as *The Bohemian Girl*.

Alfred Bunn (1796?–1860), whom *Punch* in derision nicknamed 'The Poet Bunn', claimed gentle birth, but he was not very forward with evidence for it. His chequered career, continually marked by passionate feuds of one kind or another, was that of London's two patent theatres, Drury Lane and Covent Garden, which he managed, and debased to an extraordinary degree, for a number of years until his bankruptcy in 1840. He was responsible for many slapdash adaptations of French opera, his productions a mixture of lavishness and the meanest of penny-pinching. It was said that he was not averse to pocketing his wife's earnings from friendships with noble admirers; his theatres, certainly, were little better than verminous bawdy-houses. A colourful theatrical pirate, who employed the cream of international actors, singers and composers, he could also produce reach-me-down romantic verse by the yard. He did of apoplexy.

A very different character was Michael William Balfe (1808–1870). Not only charming as a composer, he was, as his music publisher, Frederick Beale, said, 'a blue-eyed handsome little fellow, the very embodiment of sunny smiles and laughter'. He began as a violinist and baritone, appearing in Paris as Signor Balfo, and even as a boy could arrange orchestral pieces. He often sang his own compositions in drawing-rooms, and, in the catty words of Mrs Byrne in *Gossip of the Century*, 'He found it a profitable business, his terms were high, and he had a trick of disappearing as soon as he considered he had done enough for the money.' A prolific worker, Balfe wrote sixteen operas before *The Bohemian Girl*. These and his tuneful songs made him, an Irishman, England's favourite composer until the coming of Arthur Sullivan. His reputation, and especially his gift for melody, won him after his death a bust in Westminster Abbey. Several other songs by Balfe are to be found in this volume, including another piece in this section, 'Come Into the Garden, Maud'.

Incidentally, in the fifth line of 'The Dream' one cannot help but notice the original (presumably) of 'Yes, We Have No Bananas'.

Jeanie with the Light-Brown Hair

Written and composed by STEPHEN C. FOSTER

Allegretto moderato

1. I dream of Jea-nie with the light-brown hair, Borne like a va - pour on the sum-mer air; I see her trip-ping where the bright streams play, Hap - py as the dai - sies that dance on her way; Ma-ny were the wild notes her

mer-ry voice would pour, Ma-ny were the blithe birds that war - bled them o'er.

CHORUS

Oh!___ I dream of Jea-nie with the light brown hair,

I dream of Jea-nie with the light brown hair,

I dream of Jea-nie with the light brown hair,

Float-ing like a va-pour on the soft sum-mer air.

Float-ing like a va-pour on the soft sum-mer air.

Float-ing like a va-pour on the soft sum-mer air.

Jeanie with the Light-Brown Hair

1. I dream of Jeanie with the light-brown hair,
      Borne like a vapour on the summer air;
   I see her tripping where the bright streams play,
      Happy as the daisies that dance on her way;
   Many were the wild notes her merry voice would pour,
      Many were the blithe birds that warbled them o'er.

   CHORUS: Oh, I dream of Jeanie with the light brown hair,
              Floating like vapour on the soft summer air.

2. I long for Jeanie with the day-dawn smile,
      Radiant in gladness, warm with winning guile;
   I hear her melodies, like joys gone by, '
      Sighing round my heart o'er the fond hopes that die—
   Sighing like the night wind, and sobbing like the rain,
      Wailing for the lost one that comes not again.

   CHORUS: Oh, I dream of Jeanie, etc.

3. I sigh for Jeanie, but her light form stray'd
      Far from the fond hearts round her native glade,
   Her smiles have vanish'd, and her sweet songs flown,
      Flitting like the dreams that have cheer'd us and gone.
   Now nodding wild-flow'rs may wither on the shore,
      But her gentle fingers will cull them no more.

   CHORUS: Oh, I dream of Jeanie, etc.

Inspired in 1854 by Stephen Foster's wife, Jane McDowell, a doctor's daughter whom he married four years before, the song was originally entitled 'Jennie with the Light-Brown Hair'. The Fosters had an unhappy married life; they separated often, reunited and parted again. She finally found work as a telegraph operator. The ballad was not always popular. After Foster's death, the copyright was renewed for the benefit of Jane and her daughter, and for the accumulated period of nineteen years they received royalties for the sale of fifteen copies—75 cents. In its time the song was a great favourite of the Christy Minstrels.

It is a mark of our times that 'Jeanie's light-brown hair' reappeared a few years ago doing promotional duty for an American hair-colouring preparation. The song also did sterling duty in the U.S.A. late in the 1930s when it was used, seemingly ceaselessly, during the ASCAP strike when no copyrighted compositions could be played.

More details of Stephen Foster's life are to be found on page 269.

Come into the Garden, Maud

Written by ALFRED, LORD TENNYSON

Composed by M. W. BALFE

Come into the Garden, Maud

-lone. I am here,__ at the gate a - lone. And the

wood - bine spi - ces are waft - ed a-broad, And the musk of the ro - ses

blown, For a breeze of morn - ing moves,__ And the

plan-et of love is on high, Be - gin - ning to faint in the

light that she loves, On a bed of daf - fo - dil sky, To

faint in the light of the sun she loves, To faint in the light and to

die. Come!___ come!

Come in-to the gar - den Maud, For the black bat, Night, is

flown; Come in-to the gar - den, Maud, I am

here at the gate a - lone, I am here at the gate a -

Come into the Garden, Maud

-lone,   I   am   here _____ at the   gate   a -

- lone!

Queen   Rose   of   the   rose - bud,

dolce

Gar - den of girls,   Come hi -ther,   the dan - ces   are done;   In

gloss   of sa -tin   and glim -mer   of pearls, Queen   li - ly   and rose,   in

cresc.   *ff*   *f*   *dim.*   *rall.* *p*   6   6

Come into the Garden, Maud

tread, My heart would hear her and beat,
Were it

earth in an ear - thy bed,_____ Come_____

— my own, my sweet, Come_____ my own, my sweet

Maud, Maud, come, I'm here at the gate a -

- lone.

Come into the Garden, Maud

Come into the garden, Maud,
   For the black bat, Night, is flown;
Come into the garden, Maud,
   I am here at the gate alone.

And the woodbine spices are wafted abroad,
   And the musk of the roses blown,
For a breeze of morning moves,
   And the planet of love is on high,
Beginning to faint in the light that she loves,
   On a bed of daffodil sky,
To faint in the light of the sun she loves,
   To faint in the light and to die.

Come! come! Come into the garden, Maud,
   For the black bat, Night, is flown;
Come into the garden, Maud,
   I am here at the gate alone.

Queen Rose of the rosebud, Garden of girls,
   Come hither, the dances are done;
In gloss of satin and glimmer of pearls,
   Queen lily and rose, in one.
Shine out little head sunning over with curls
   To the flowers and be their Sun.
Shine out! Shine out! and be their Sun.

Come into the garden, Maud,
   For the black bat, Night, is flown;
Come into the garden, Maud.

She is coming, my own, my sweet,
   Were it ever so airy a tread,
My heart would hear her and beat,
   Were it earth in an earthy bed,
Come my own, my sweet,
Come my own, my sweet,
   Maud, Maud, come, I'm here at the gate alone.

This most hackneyed of parlour war-horses still has charm enough to hold an audience. The relief of the return to the C major of the last verse is very real after the dramatic, if harmonically ingenuous quasi-recitative of 'Shine out!' The piece was written specially for the tenor, Sims Reeves, at the suggestion of the music publisher John Boosey. Balfe composed the song in Paris in 1857 and posted off the opening bars to Reeves. A few days later Balfe had them back with the scribbled superscription: 'This will do.—S.R.' Reeves should have been a little more careful, for the piece is by no means an impeccable setting. Balfe paid scant attention to the meaning of Tennyson's words, and Charles E. Pearce, Sims Reeves's biographer, pointed out: '. . . the hash which the composer, with his habitual indifference to poetic rhythm when it interfered with his melody, made of "Queen rose of the rosebud garden of girls", turning it into "Queen of the rosebud, garden of girls", and making it still further nonsensical by dividing the line into two phrases'.

One story which indicates the song's sedate reputation is that of the music-hall star, Marie Lloyd; she was determined to prove that smut only exists in the mind of the beholder, and sang it to a bench of magistrates with all the sly innuendo at her command, turning it in the process into the bluest of ballads.

There is a short biography of M. W. Balfe on page 35.

Touch the Harp Gently

Written by SAMUEL N. MITCHELL

Composed by CHARLES BLAMPHIN

1. Just touch the harp gent - ly, my pret - ty Lou - ise, And sing me the songs that I love;____ They will call back the days when to - ge - ther we sat On the

porch 'neath the nest of the dove._____ There was one that you sang, my pret-ty Lou-ise, It brings fond re-col-lec-tions to me. You re- - mem - ber the mock-ing-bird mi-mick'd it once As it perch'd on the sy-ca-more tree;_____ Just touch the harp gent-ly, my

ad lib.

pp

Touch the Harp Gently

pret-ty Lou-ise, Just touch the harp gent-ly, Lou - ise ____

CHORUS

Oh! touch the harp gent-ly, my pret-ty Lou-ise, And

sing me the songs that I love,____ They will call back the days, when to -

- ge-ther we sat On the porch 'neath the nest of the dove.____

Touch the Harp Gently

1. Just touch the harp gently, my pretty Louise,
   And sing me the songs that I love;
They will call back the days when together we sat
   On the porch 'neath the nest of the dove.
There was one that you sang, my pretty Louise,
   It brings fond recollections to me,
You remember the mocking bird mimick'd it once
   As it perch'd on the sycamore tree;
Just touch the harp gently, my pretty Louise,
Just touch the harp gently, Louise.

CHORUS: Oh, touch the harp gently, my pretty Louise,
   And sing me the songs that I love,
      They will call back the days when together we sat
      On the porch 'neath the nest of the dove.

2. Just touch the harp gently, my pretty Louise,
   And sing me the songs that I love;
They'll recall the bright days when we play'd in the wood,
   And watch'd the birds flitting above.
There was one that you sang, my pretty Louise,
   The words, I remember them well,
I lov'd it, and when you had finished each verse,
   I kiss'd you and said: 'Never tell';
Just touch the harp gently, my pretty Louise,
Just touch the harp gently, Louise.

CHORUS: Oh, touch the harp gently, etc.

Charles Blamphin (1830 or 31–1895) was a well-known English harpist who also composed ballads. One in particular caught the popular favour in its day, 'Bonnie Scotland, I Adore Thee'.

Oh Mother! Take the Wheel Away

Written and composed by CLARIBEL

1. Oh, mo-ther, take the wheel a-way, and put it out of sight, For I am hea-vy heart-ed, and I can-not spin to-night: Come near-er, near-er yet, I have a stor-y for your ear, So

Oh Mother! Take the Wheel Away

1. Oh, mother, take the wheel away, and put it out of sight,
       For I am heavy hearted, and I cannot spin tonight:
   Come nearer, nearer yet, I have a story for your ear,
       So come and sit beside me, come and listen, mother dear;
   You heard the village bells, tonight, his wedding bells they were;
       And Mabel is his happy wife, and I am lonely here;
   A year ago tonight, I mind, he sought me for his bride,
       And who so glad at heart as I, that happy Easter tide?

2. But Mabel came among us, and her face was fair to see,
       What wonder was it, mother, that he thought no more of me?
   When first he said fair words to her, I know she did not hear,
       But in the end she listen'd, could she help it, mother dear?
   And afterwards we met, and we were friendly all the same:
       For ne'er a word I said to them of anger, or of blame,
   'Till both believed I did not care, and may be they were right,
       But mother, take the wheel away, I cannot spin tonight.

Here is the languishing maiden at her most Victorian, for to compete with a rival would have been unacceptably forward. This 'jilt' song is representative of the ballads of unrequited and rejected love which increased in favour as the century moved on, especially in the music-hall. The music is notably subservient to the sentiment.

'Claribel' was the name under which Mrs Charlotte Alington Barnard (1830–1869) wrote both words and music of more than a hundred songs. Her musical education was sketchy, although she received singing lessons from Madame Sainton-Dolby among others. In the last ten years of her short life she crammed not only her songs but published two volumes of verse. She is credited with having introduced the royalty system for ballads. Probably far more appreciated in America than her native England, Claribel is now almost completely forgotten, except for 'Come Back to Erin', which many imagine to be a folk song. Unkind commentators have called her songs vapid, but she was certainly completely in tune with the taste of her period.

When You and I were Young, Maggie

Written by GEORGE W. JOHNSON

Composed by J. A. BUTTERFIELD

1. I wan-dered to-day to the hill, Mag-gie, To watch the scene be-low; The creek and the creak-ing old mill, Maggie, As we used to long a-go. The green grove is gone from the

When You and I were Young, Maggie

hill, Mag-gie, Where first the____ dai - sies sprung; The

creak-ing old mill is ___ still, Mag-gie, Since you and I were young.

CHORUS

And now we are a - ged and gray, Mag-gie, And the tri - als of life near-ly

And now we are a - ged and gray, Mag-gie, And the tri - als of life near-ly

And now we are a - ged and gray, Mag-gie, And the tri - als of life near-ly

And now we are a - ged and gray, Mag-gie, And the tri - als of life near-ly

When You and I were Young, Maggie

1. I wandered today to the hill, Maggie,
   To watch the scene below;
   The creek and the creaking old mill, Maggie,
   As we used to long ago,
   The green grove is gone from the hill, Maggie,
   Where first the daisies sprung;
   The creaking old mill is still, Maggie,
   Since you and I were young.

CHORUS: And now we are aged and gray, Maggie,
   And the trials of life nearly done;
   Let us sing of the days that are gone, Maggie,
   When you and I were young.

2. A city so silent and lone, Maggie,
   Where the young and the gay and the best,
   In polish'd white mansions of stone, Maggie,
   Have each found a place of rest,
   Is built where the birds used to play, Maggie,
   And join in the songs that were sung;
   For we sang as gay as they, Maggie,
   When you and I were young.

CHORUS: And now we are aged and gray, Maggie, etc.

3. They say I am feeble with age, Maggie,
   My steps are less sprightly than then,
   My face is a well-written page, Maggie,
   But time alone was the pen.
   They say we are aged and gray, Maggie,
   As spray by the white breakers flung;
   But to me, you're as fair as you were, Maggie,
   When you and I were young.

CHORUS: And now we are aged and gray, Maggie, etc.

The heroine of this most fetching and lilting of ballads actually lived—and died. She was Maggie Clark, a girl courted by her schoolteacher, who wrote this lyric, and he celebrated, too, a real mill and a real creek in Canada. George W. Johnson (1839–1917) was a scholar with a Ph.D. from Johns Hopkins University. He and Maggie married in 1865 and moved to Cleveland, Ohio, where, tragically, she died in the same year. The song was published a year later. Johnson returned to Canada and spent the rest of his life at Toronto University.

J. A. Butterfield (1837–1891) was a violinist, singer and music teacher. He settled in Chicago where he started a publishing business. This song, his one great success, has a freshness and charmingly naive quality of obvious appeal to the amateur—who is helped by its restricted vocal range, one octave and two notes.

Twickenham Ferry

Written and composed by THEO. MARZIALS

1. "O hoi ye-ho, Ho-ye-ho, Who's for the fer-ry? (The bri-ar's in bud, the___ sun go-ing down), And I'll row ye so quick and I'll row___ ye so steady, And 'tis but a pen-ny to Twick-en-ham Town." The fer-ry-man's slim and the

58

fer - ry-man's young And he's just a soft twang in the
turn of his tongue, And he's fresh as a pip - pin and
brown as a ber-ry, And 'tis but a pen - ny to Twick - en-ham Town.
O-
- hoi - ye - ho, Ho - ye - ho Ho - ye - ho, Ho.

Twickenham Ferry

1. 'O-hoi ye-ho, Ho-ye-ho, Who's for the ferry?
     (The briar's in bud, the sun going down),
   And I'll row ye so quick and I'll row ye so steady,
     And 'tis but a penny to Twickenham Town.'
   The ferryman's slim and the ferryman's young
     And he's just a soft twang in the turn of his tongue,
   And he's fresh as a pippin and brown as a berry,
     And 'tis but a penny to Twickenham Town.
   O-hoi ye-ho, Ho-ye-ho, Ho-ye-ho, Ho.

2. 'O-hoi ye-ho, Ho-ye-ho, I'm for the ferry,
     (The briar's in bud, the sun going down),
   And it's late as it is and I haven't a penny,
     And how shall I get me to Twickenham Town?'
   She'd a rose in her bonnet, and oh! she look'd sweet
     As the little pink flower that grows in the wheat,
   With her cheeks like a rose and her lips like a cherry,
     'And sure and you're welcome to Twickenham Town.'
   O-hoi ye-ho, Ho-ye-ho, Ho-ye-ho, Ho.

3. O-hoi ye-ho, Ho, you're too late for the ferry
     (The briar's in bud, the sun going down),
   And he's not rowing quick and he's not rowing steady,
     You'd think 'twas a journey to Twickenham Town.
   'O hoi, and O ho,' you may call as you will,
     The moon is a-rising on Petersham Hill,
   And with love like a rose in the stern of the wherry,
     There's danger in crossing to Twickenham Town.
   O-hoi ye-ho, Ho-ye-ho, Ho-ye-ho, Ho.

'The song of the season, a perfect gem!' said *Musical Jottings*. There was quite a rage for 'river songs' just at the time, and to this category belong Milton Wellings's 'At the Ferry' and 'The Old Lock' with words by Fred W. Weatherly. Additionally it uses the folk-song idiom, just becoming fashionable, allied to a dance-like simplicity: a gem, indeed.

Theo., short for Théophile, Marzials (1850–1920) came from French Huguenot stock, but was born of an English mother in a train, he said, somewhere between Paris and Brussels. It is believed that he was distantly related to the Brontës. He studied music in Paris and Milan and for many years was on the staff of the British Museum. A prolific composer of charming songs, he was no mean lyricist either. He wrote the words of several songs for Goring Thomas and provided him with the libretto for his opera, *Esmeralda*. As a composer, he set poems by Elizabeth Barrett Browning and Swinburne. In later years, although he was writing as well as ever, he fell out of public favour. His last letter to his publisher ran: 'Thanks for your cheque, it won't make me much richer nor you much poorer, thank God!'

Love's Old Sweet Song

Written by J. CLIFTON BINGHAM

Composed by JAMES L. MOLLOY

Once in the dear dead days be-yond re-call, When on the world the mists be-gan to fall, Out of the dreams that rose in hap-py throng, Low to our hearts Love sung an old sweet song; And in the dusk where

Love's Old Sweet Song

1. Once in the dear dead days beyond recall,
   When on the world the mists began to fall,
   Out of the dreams that rose in happy throng,
   Low to our hearts Love sung an old sweet song;
   And in the dusk where fell the firelight gleam,
   Softly it wove itself into our dream.

CHORUS: Just a song at twilight, when the lights are low,
   And the flick'ring shadows softly come and go,
   Tho' the heart be weary, sad the day and long,
   Still to us at twilight comes Love's old song,
   Comes Love's old sweet song.

2. Even today we hear Love's song of yore,
   Deep in our hearts it dwells for evermore,
   Footsteps may falter, weary grows the way,
   Still we can hear it at the close of day;
   Still to the end when life's dim shadows fall,
   Love will be found the sweetest song of all.

CHORUS: Just a song at twilight, etc.

Sir Arthur Sullivan was once accused of appropriating the first two bars of this song as the opening for a number in *The Gondoliers*. He shrugged it off with the remark: 'We had only eight notes between us.'

This ballad was not written, as one might have thought, at twilight, but at four o'clock on a February morning in 1882, by J. Clifton Bingham (1859–1913), a professional lyricist. He reported that various composers vied for the privilege of setting his poem to music. Molloy won by being the first to contact him via the electric telegraph. The person who probably made most money out of the song was the soprano, Madame Antoinette Sterling, who received a large royalty for several years for having introduced it to the public.

James Lyman Molloy (1837–1909) graduated from the Catholic university in Dublin, studied in London, Paris and Bonn, and was called to the English bar. Not very active as a lawyer, however, he found a more congenial occupation in exercising his fine voice and composing songs. His first success was with 'Beer, Beer, Beautiful Beer' from one of his three operettas, and others of his hundred or so ballads were 'The Old Cottage Clock', 'Darby and Joan', 'The Kerry Dance' and 'Tomorrow Will be Friday and We've Caught No Fish Today'. A real professional, he took immense pains to get his songs exactly right for performance, revising and making little improvements until they reached the stage of St James's Hall at a ballad concert. He edited a collection of Irish songs and was also a notable sportsman, rowing up and down the rivers of France.

That is Love

Written and composed by FELIX MCGLENNON

1. Love,　sweet love is the po-et's theme,＿＿

Love,　sweet love, is the po-et's dream;＿＿　What　is the love of which they

sing?＿＿＿　On-ly　a phan-tom, un-real thing!

That is Love

'Tis but the dalli - ance, the dalliance of youth and maid,

Tis but the pas - sion, the passion and vows that fade;

'Tis not the Heav'n, the Heav'n im-plant - ing glow That

true hearts call love, ah, no! ah no! See a moth-er gaz-ing on her

ba - by boy, With ec-stat-ic eyes and heart that fills with joy,

He to her is pur-est gold with-out al-loy, For him how she prays to Heav'n a-

- bove. How she guides his foot-steps through this

vale of strife, Watch-es o'er his bed-side when in -

rit.

-fec - tion's rife, Risk-ing for her ba - by boy her

Tempo Imo

health, her life, That is love, that is love! _____

That is Love

1. Love, sweet love is the poet's theme,
    Love, sweet love is the poet's dream;
  What is the love of which they sing?
    Only a phantom, unreal thing!
  'Tis but the dalliance, the dalliance of youth and maid,
    'Tis but the passion, the passion and vows that fade;
  'Tis not the Heav'n, the Heav'n implanting glow
    That true hearts call love, ah, no! ah, no!

        See a mother gazing on her baby boy,
        With ecstatic eyes and heart that fills with joy,
        He to her is purest gold without alloy,
            For him how she prays to Heav'n above.
        How she guides his footsteps through this vale of strife,
        Watches o'er his bedside when infection's rife,
        Risking for her baby boy her health, her life,
            That is love, that is love!

2. Love, sweet love, how the word's misplaced,
    Love, sweet love, how the theme's disgraced;
  What is a fond lover's ardent glance?
    What is a maiden's shy advance?
  What is the pressure, the pressure of am'rous lips!
    What is the pressure, the pressure of finger tips?
  Only the pleasure of a passing day,
    'Tis not the love that will live for aye!

        See a father standing at his cottage door,
        Watching baby in the gutter rolling o'er,
        Laughing at his merry pranks, but hark, a roar,
            Help, oh, help him, gracious Heav'n above.
        Dashing down the road there comes a maddened horse,
        Out the father rushes with resistless force,
        Saves the child, but he lies there a mangled corpse,
            That is love, that is love!

3. Oh! the love of a faithful friend,
    True, true love that will never end;
  Where can such friendship be found on earth?
    In true hearts above it findeth birth.
  Friends meet friends and they vow, they vow to cling,
    Often, alas! does their love, their love take wing;
  Seldom, alas! can faithful friendship be,
    As that of two comrades who went to sea.

When a squall had struck the ship and she was lost,
Clinging to a plank the chums were tempest tost,
But the plank was water-logged and sunk almost,
　　One of them must meet his God above.
One of them said, 'Jack, this plank will not hold two,
You've a wife and children, so I'll die for you.
Good-bye, Jack,' he leaves the plank and sinks from view,
　　That is love, that is love!

4. Love, sweet love, not the passion's glow,
　　That some call love on earth below,
No! but the pure, the undying love,
　　The sacred affection from above.
'Tis not the love, the love for a beauteous face,
　　'Tis not the love that Time's ravages soon will chase;
'Tis not the love from brightly sparkling eyes,
　　No! 'tis the love sent from Paradise.

　　See a husband parting from a darling wife,
　　Bearing arms for England, mid the battle's strife,
　　Gazing on her portrait where the foes are rife,
　　　　Treasuring a lock of hair, a glove.
　　See the wife from whom the husband had to part,
　　News has come, he's fallen—how the tear-drops start.
　　How she droops and then dies of a broken heart.
　　　　That is love, that is love!

This ballad repays dramatic (but intensely serious) rendition. Notice the passionate possibilities of the musical phrase, 'Risking for her baby boy her health, *her life*,' followed by the impressive statement in tempo primo, 'That is love.'

Felix McGlennon (died 1943) was an Irishman who wrote the words and music of a very large number of music-hall songs, among them the famous 'Comrades' of 1891, in the last quarter of the nineteenth century. Some of them, including 'That is Love' and 'The Ship I Love' in our next section, graduated from the stage to respectability in the parlour, albeit the lower middle-class parlour. His ballads were popular in America, too, and when he visited the States, where, like Mark Twain, newspapers had falsely reported his death, he wrote the saucy lyric of Monroe H. Rosenfeld's 'The Golden Hair was Hanging Down Her Back'. Extremely businesslike, he was always on the look-out for promising young singers who could buy and promote his songs. He was somewhat of a dandy, too.

The Rosary

Written by ROBERT CAMERON ROGERS

Composed by ETHELBERT NEVIN

1. The hours I spent with thee, dear heart, Are as a string of pearls to me; I count them o-ver ev-'ry one a-part, My ro-sa-ry, my ro-sa-ry!

2. Each hour a pearl, each pearl a pray'r To still a heart in ab-sence wrung: I tell each bead un-to the

end, And there a Cross is hung! 3. O mem-o-ries that bless and

burn! O, bar-ren gain and bit-ter loss!

I kiss each bead, and strive at last to learn To kiss the

Cross, sweet-heart! To kiss the Cross.

The Rosary

1. The hours I spent with thee, dear heart,
    Are as a string of pearls to me;
  I count them over ev'ry one apart,
    My rosary, my rosary!

2. Each hour a pearl, each pearl a pray'r
    To still a heart in absence wrung:
  I tell each bead unto the end,
    And there a Cross is hung!

3. O memories that bless and burn!
    O, barren gain and bitter loss!
  I kiss each bead, and strive at last to learn
    To kiss the Cross, sweetheart!
    To kiss the Cross.

With its high-minded note of religiosity and superior drawing-room style, 'The Rosary' belongs to the genus 'art song' of the 'nineties (it was written in 1898), as distinct from the tear-jerking productions of New York's Tin Pan Alley, which was booming at this time. The words of the ballad were published four years previously in a volume of verse by Robert Cameron Rogers (1862–1912), a journalist and poet who was born in Buffalo.

Ethelbert Woodbridge Nevin (1862–1901) studied in Pittsburgh, near where he was born, Boston and Berlin. He had ambitions to become a concert pianist, but it was plain after his debut in Pittsburgh that his talent was that of a vocal composer. He had an astonishing gift for judging the public's taste for the delicate and lilting. His many songs included 'Little Boy Blue' and the 'coon' ballad, 'Mighty Lak' a Rose', written in the last year of his life. Another famous piece was the light orchestral item, 'Narcissus'.

'The Rosary' is not the composer's best work, and it requires a high standard of performance. The recit-arioso style can be a little dull even when rendered by a good singer: badly sung it is insufferable.

Soldiers & Sailors

or, Songs of Battle and the Deep

The Soldier's Tear

Written by THOMAS HAYNES BAYLY

Composed by ALEXANDER LEE

1. Up - on the hill he turn'd, To take a last fond look Of the

The Soldier's Tear

val – ley and the vil – lage church, And the cot -tage by— the

brook; He lis-ten'd to the sounds,— So fa - mi - liar to his

ear, And the sol -dier leant up -on his sword, And wip'd a – way a

tear.

sf   *dim.*

The Soldier's Tear

1. Upon the hill he turn'd,
      To take a last fond look
   Of the valley and the village church,
      And the cottage by the brook;
   He listen'd to the sounds,
      So familiar to his ear,
   And the soldier leant upon his sword,
      And wip'd away a tear.

2. Beside that cottage porch
      A girl was on her knees,
   She held aloft a snowy scarf
      Which flutter'd in the breeze;
   She breath'd a pray'r for him,
      A pray'r he could not hear,
   But he paus'd to bless her as she knelt,
      And wip'd away a tear.

3. He turn'd and left the spot
      Oh! do not deem him weak,
   For dauntless was the soldier's heart,
      Tho' tears were on his cheek;
   Go watch the foremost ranks
      In danger's dark career,
   Be sure the hand most daring there
      Has wip'd away a tear.

The setting is unpretentious but it has distinct charm, with (in the original orchestral version) its bugles in the introduction and horns, everlasting symbols of the pastoral, under 'And the soldier leant upon his sword'.

George Alexander Lee (1802–1852) was a popular and tasteful composer of ballads who also appeared as a tenor. Balfe was one of his pupils. His actress wife, Mrs Waylett, was a favourite soprano, and her renderings of her husband's songs helped to make them known. Her death so grieved Lee that he did not long survive her.

There are notes on Thomas Haynes Bayly on page 31.

Yes, Let Me Like a Soldier Fall

(from *Maritana*)

Written by EDWARD FITZBALL

Composed by VINCENT WALLACE

1. Yes! let me like a Sol - dier fall, Up - on some o - pen

plain, This breast ex-pand-ing for the ball To

blot out ev'-ry stain. Brave man-ly hearts con-

-fer my doom That gent - ler one___ may tell How-

-e'er for-got, un-known my tomb, I like a Sol-dier

Yes, Let Me Like a Soldier Fall

fell, How e'er for - got, un - known my tomb I like a
Sol - dier fell. I like a Sol - dier fell.

2. I on - ly ask of that proud race, Which ends its blaze in me, To die the last, and not dis - grace Its an - cient chiv - al - ry! Tho' o'er my clay no ban - ner wave, Nor trump - et re - qui - em swell, E -

Yes, Let Me Like a Soldier Fall

-nough they mur - mur o'er my grave He like a Sol - dier

fell, E - nough they mur - mur o'er my grave He like a

Sol - dier fell, He like a Sol - dier fell.

Yes! Let Me Like a Soldier Fall

1. Yes! let me like a Soldier fall,
    Upon some open plain,
   This breast expanding for the ball
    To blot out ev'ry stain.
   Brave manly hearts confer my doom
    That gentler one may tell
   Howe'er forgot, unknown my tomb,
    I like a Soldier fell,
   Howe'er forgot, unknown my tomb,
    I like a Soldier fell.

2. I only ask of that proud race,
    Which ends its blaze in me,
   To die the last, and not disgrace
    Its ancient chivalry!
   Tho' o'er my clay no banner wave,
    Nor trumpet requiem swell,
   Enough they murmur o'er my grave
    He like a Soldier fell,
   Enough they murmur o'er my grave
    He like a Soldier fell.

This excellent song fully repays a robust, but sensitive performance. All the paraphernalia of war in the introduction leads to a dramatic and extremely happy setting. Note how, from the sweet, murmuring accompaniment of 'Howe'er forgot, unknown my tomb', we are woken by the bugle in 'I like a soldier fell', just as though the singer has been brought back to consciousness with a jolt.

Maritana of 1845 was one of the English operas produced to such great applause by Alfred Bunn. Fitzball, who was a highly successful librettist by the mid-'forties, heard a relatively unknown Irishman, Vincent Wallace, play some of his own music. Fitzball immediately handed him the book of *Maritana* to set. The plot was not original, but a reworking of the melodrama, *Don Caesar de Bazan*, but that did not diminish the appeal of such famous arias as 'Yes, Let Me Like a Soldier Fall' and 'Scenes That are Brightest'. Although London was not noted as a nursery for grand opera, the piece was enthusiastically received on the Continent. So much so, in fact, that the Italians made their own adaptation which, in time, appeared in London. It opened during the season of 1881 at Her Majesty's Theatre. The *Musical Times* takes up the story:

> This establishment closed on the 11th ult., the only event of any importance since our last notice being the production of the Italian version of Wallace's opera, *Maritana*, with recitatives especially written for the occasion by Signor Tito Mattei. Anything which can disguise the words of the original libretto by Fitzball is undoubtedly of advantage to the effect of the work in performance.

William Vincent Wallace (1814–1865), of Irish birth, was generally agreed to be one of Britain's best native operatic composers on the strength of *Maritana*, but he was a violinist and pianist of ability as well. *Maritana* is the only one of his operas now remembered at all, but almost equal in its content of vocal gems is *Lurline*. Wallace also composed for the pianoforte.

A short biography of Edward Fitzball is printed on page 26.

Weeping, Sad and Lonely

(When this Cruel War is Over)

Written by CHARLES C. SAWYER   Composed by HENRY TUCKER

1. Dear - est love, do you re - mem - ber, When we last did meet,

How you told me that you loved____ me, Kneel - ing at my

feet? Oh! how proud you stood be - fore____ me

In your _ suit of blue,____ When you vow'd to me and

coun - try Ev - er to be true.

Weeping, Sad and Lonely

Weeping, Sad and Lonely

1. Dearest love, do you remember,
   When we last did meet,
   How you told me that you loved me,
   Kneeling at my feet?
   Oh! how proud you stood before me
   In your suit of blue,
   When you vow'd to me and country
   Ever to be true.

CHORUS: Weeping, sad and lonely,
   Hopes and fears how vain!
   Yet praying,
   When this cruel war is over,
   Praying that we meet again!

2. When the summer breeze is sighing
   Mournfully along;
   Or when autumn leaves are falling,
   Sadly breathes the song.
   Oft in dreams I see thee lying
   On the battle plain,
   Lonely, wounded, even dying,
   Calling, but in vain.

CHORUS: Weeping, sad and lonely, etc.

3. If amid the din of battle
   Nobly you should fall,
   Far away from those who love you,
   None to hear you call—
   Who would whisper words of comfort,
   Who would soothe your pain?
   Ah! the many cruel fancies
   Ever in my brain.

CHORUS: Weeping, sad and lonely, etc.

4. But your country called you, darling,
   Angels cheer your way;
   While our nation's sons are fighting,
   We can only pray.
   Nobly strike for God and liberty,
   Let all nations see
   How we love the starry banner,
   Emblem of the free.

CHORUS: Weeping, sad and lonely, etc.

Charles Carroll Sawyer also wrote and composed the equally lugubrious 'Who Will Care for Mother Now?' Songs of a similar nature were the speciality of Henry Tucker; his 'Dear Mother, I've Come Home to Die' appears on page 314, together with a concise biography. Sawyer himself described how this Civil War ballad came to be written:

During the year 1861–2, many songs were published, but they were all filled with the love of the soldier for those whom he had left at home, and, thinking it would cheer and comfort our brave boys, I composed and published the song 'When This Cruel War is Over', which seemed to reach the hearts of both armies, so that in a few months I found it almost impossible to supply the demand. The song reached the unprecedented sale of nearly one million copies.

The poet would seem to us to have an odd idea of comforts for the troops, and this opinion was obviously shared by the commanders of the Army of the Potomac for they forbade their soldiers to sing it in case it lowered morale. Of marked pacifist intent, it was answered by a parody, 'Yes I Would the Cruel War Were Over', which contained the lines:

> Would the cruel work were done
> With my country undivided
> And the battle fought and won.
> Let the contest now before us
> Be decided by the sword,
> For the war cannot be ended
> Till the Union is restored.

The theme reappeared, in somewhat less elegant form fifty years later, to the tune of the hymn, 'What a Friend We Have in Jesus', sung by British soldiers in the trenches during the Kaiser's War:

> When this lousy war is over,
> No more soldiering for me,
> When I get my civvy clothes on,
> Oh, how happy I shall be!
> No more church parades on Sundays,
> No more putting in for leave,
> I shall kiss the Sergeant-Major,
> How I'll miss him, how he'll grieve.

The words and music of 'Weeping, Sad and Lonely' complement each other perfectly. The pathetic nature of the first phrase sets the tone for what follows: it is a technical masterpiece, guaranteed never to fail in inducing the ready tear.

The Old Brigade

Written by FRED E. WEATHERLY

Composed by ODOARDO BARRI

The Old Brigade

Fought till they fell and died! Who so ready and un-dis-mayed? Who so mer-ry and true? Where are the boys of the old Bri-gade? Where are the lads we knew? Then stead-i-ly shoul-der to shoul-der, Stead-i-ly blade by blade! Rea-dy and strong,

marching a-long Like the boys of the old Bri - gade! _____ Then
stead - i -ly ___ shoul-der to shoul - der, Stead-i -ly ___ blade _ by ___
blade! Rea - dy and strong, march - ing a - long Like the
boys of the old bri - gade.
2. O - ver the sea far a - way -they lie,

The Old Brigade

Far from the land of their love;___ Na - tions al - ter, the years go by, But Heav'n still is Heav'n a - bove.___ Not in the ab - bey proud - ly laid Find they a place or part; The gal - lant boys of the old Bri - gade, They sleep in old Eng - land's heart. Then stead - i - ly___ shoul - der to shoul - der, Stead - i - ly___ blade___ by___

The Old Brigade

1. Where are the boys of the old Brigade,
      Who fought with us side by side?.
   Shoulder to shoulder, and blade by blade,
      Fought till they fell and died!
   Who so ready and undismayed?
      Who so merry and true?
   Where are the boys of the old Brigade?
      Where are the lads we knew?

   CHORUS:
   Then steadily shoulder to shoulder,
   Steadily blade by blade!
   Ready and strong, marching along
   Like the boys of the old Brigade!

2. Over the sea far away they lie,
      Far from the land of their love;
   Nations alter, the years go by,
      But Heav'n is still Heav'n above,
   Not in the abbey proudly laid
      Find they a place or part;
   The gallant boys of the old Brigade,
      They sleep in old England's heart.

   CHORUS:
   Then steadily shoulder to shoulder, etc.

One of parlour balladry's most prolific and deft of lyricists, Fred E. Weatherly (1848–1929), is well represented in this volume. His 'Nancy Lee' appears later in this section, and there is also his 'Auntie' under the heading of 'Boys and Girls'. One of thirteen children, he was educated at Hereford Cathedral School and Brasenose College, Oxford, where the aesthetic Walter Pater was his tutor. Weatherly's tastes, though, tended towards athleticism, and he coxed and rode. At Oxford, where he spent twenty years as undergraduate and crammer to dull boys, he met Dr Thomas Arnold's three daughters, who, as he reported in his autobiography, were 'very clever and superior. But they sometimes unbent and would condescend to play games, though of course very difficult games'.

He published a book of poems before graduation, receiving the approbation of Mr Gladstone, and his muse kept him busy with songs, verses, children's books 'and some verses for Christmas cards, but not mottoes for crackers. I drew the line there.' At the age of thirty-nine he was called to the Bar and became interested in the legal aspects of copyright. He wrote a book about it, and sued the famous Copinger when the latter lifted a long paragraph from his writing without acknowledgement. Meanwhile, he was also writing for the theatre, and supplied English versions of Mascagni's *Cavalleria Rusticana*, Leoncavallo's *Pagliacci* and other operas. It is Weatherly's words that we recognise when we hear: 'On with the motley, the paint and the powder.' A certain 'distinguished English singer' thought the version so good that he asked the poet 'how I managed to find so good an Italian translation of my words'. Literally thousands 'of songs flowed from his pen and about fifteen hundred were published, among them such famous pieces as 'Danny Boy', 'Nancy Lee', 'The Old Brigade', 'Roses of Picardy' and 'Star of Bethlehem'. This cheerful and self-satisfied pundit married twice, took silk, and, in his seventy-seventh year wrote a highly entertaining autobiography, *Piano and Gown*.

The composer of 'The Old Brigade', Odoardo Barri (1844–1920), was really Edward Slater. He wrote the music of a number of songs popular in their time, 'The River and the Maiden', 'The Land of Dreams' and a vocal waltz entitled 'Song of the Gout', which *Musical Jottings* found 'neither a pleasant subject or a pleasing song'.

Tom Bowling

Written and composed by CHARLES DIBDIN

1. Here, a sheer hulk, lies poor Tom Bow-ling, The dar-ling of our crew,_____ No more he'll hear the tem-pest how-ling For

Tom Bowling

Tom Bowling

1. Here, a sheer hulk, lies poor Tom Bowling,
    The darling of our crew,
No more he'll hear the tempest howling
    For death has broach'd him to.
His form was of the manliest beauty,
    His heart was kind and soft!
Faithful below he did his duty,
    And now he's gone aloft,
    And now he's gone aloft!

2. Tom never from his word departed,
    His virtues were so rare,
His friends were many, and true-hearted,
    His Poll was kind and fair:
And then he'd sing so blithe and jolly,
    Ah many's the time and oft!
But mirth is turned to melancholy,
    For Tom is gone aloft,
    For Tom is gone aloft.

3. Yet shall poor Tom find pleasant weather,
    When He, who all commands,
Shall give, to call life's crew together,
    The word to pipe all hands:
Thus death, who kings and tars dispatches,
    In vain Tom's life has doff'd,
For though his body's under hatches,
    His soul is gone aloft,
    His soul is gone aloft!

There was an original of this noble Tar, the composer's elder brother, Tom, captain of a vessel in the Indian service, who died at sea after having been struck by lightning. His death occurred when Charles Dibdin was a boy; he was idealised and immortalised many years later by this song which was originally known as 'Poor Tom Bowling'. It is written in a style of somewhat facetious metaphor popular at the beginning of the nineteenth century—Thomas Hood was particularly addicted to it—but, with the superb melody, Dibdin completely transcends it. Notice Tom going aloft in the music at the end of each verse. The whole is a masterpiece of wry and moving humour, with an elegiac note that kept it long in the Victorian drawing-room repertoire.

Charles Dibdin (1745–1814) was a self-made man of multifarious activities. He sang, acted, wrote dramas, composed and played upon the violin and organ. His life was rather irregular, and he fell out with David Garrick, the famous actor-manager, when the former abandoned Harriet Pitt, a dancer with whom he had formed an illicit union. So much did his idealisation of the British Tar gain official approval that he was granted in 1802 an annual pension of £200. It is, too, as a musical entertainer that he is of interest in the history of popular song. He toured England with his programmes of 'Reading and Music' and 'Table Entertainments', presenting them in an engagingly informal and unstagy manner. He accompanied himself 'on an instrument of a peculiar kind, combining the properties of the pianoforte and the chamber organ', and to this curious machine were attached bells, side-drum, tambourine and gong.

As well as being the father of the jolly Jack Tar, Dibdin is also credited with the popularisation of the comic Negro. He played the part of Mungo in his opera, *The Padlock*, a piece that was also successful in America and undoubtedly had some influence on early black-face impersonators.

Dibdin had two illegitimate sons, Charles and Tom. They were both involved in the theatre, and the latter wrote, when England was threatened by Napoleonic invasion, 'The Snug Little Island', with its immortal lines:

> Oh, what a snug little Island,
> A right little, tight little Island . . .

Rocked in the Cradle of the Deep

Written by EMMA HART WILLARD

Composed by JOSEPH P. KNIGHT

1. Rock'd in the cra-dle of the deep, I lay me down in peace to sleep. Se-cure, I rest up-on the wave, For Thou, O Lord, hast pow-er to save. I

Rocked in the Cradle of the Deep

know Thou wilt not slight my call, For Thou dost mark the spar - row's

fall, And calm and peace-ful is my sleep, _____

Rock'd in the cra - dle of the deep; And calm and peace-ful is my

sleep, _____ Rock'd in the cra - dle of the deep.

last verse
D.S.

Rocked in the Cradle of the Deep

1. Rock'd in the cradle of the deep,
   I lay me down in peace to sleep.
   Secure, I rest upon the wave,
   For Thou, O Lord, hast power to save.
   I know Thou wilt not slight my call,
   For Thou dost mark the sparrow's fall,
   And calm and peaceful is my sleep,
   Rock'd in the cradle of the deep;
   And calm and peaceful is my sleep,
   Rock'd in the cradle of the deep.

2. And such the trust that still were mine,
   Tho' stormy winds swept o'er the brine;
   Or tho' the tempest's fiery breath
   Rous'd me from sleep to wreck and death,
   In Ocean cave still safe with Thee,
   The hope of immortality;
   And calm and peaceful is my sleep, etc.

Supposedly inspired by a view of the Bristol Channel, this song was written by Mrs Willard, the famous educator, while crossing the Atlantic on her way home from Europe in 1832. The Duc de Choiseul, who was on board the same vessel, set the words to music, but it was J. P. Knight's setting that became associated with the poem. This was the favourite song of the basso profundo, until rivalled by 'Asleep in the Deep', written by Arthur Lamb and H. W. Petrie at the end of the nineteenth century.

Emma Hart Willard (1787–1870) was encouraged as a child by her parents to high thinking, and she grew up into a very formidable lady indeed. After some experience as a teacher, she opened her own school at Middlebury, Vermont, in 1814, demonstrating that, contrary to general belief, young ladies' minds would not be overstrained by acquainting them with mathematics and philosophy. She campaigned vigorously for equal educational advantages for women and was constantly improving teaching methods. As well as textbooks, she also wrote other verse of similar quality to 'Rocked in the Cradle of the Deep'.

The composer, J. P. Knight, some notes on whom appear on page 31, was teaching music at Mrs Willard's school when he set this poem to its well-known tune. His long, languid phrases are an apt reflection of the lullaby atmosphere of the text.

A Life on the Ocean Wave

Written by EPES SARGENT (after S. J. ARNOLD)   Composed by HENRY RUSSELL

101

life on the o - cean wave!___ A___ home on the roll - ing deep!___Where the

scat - ter'd wa - ters rave,___And the winds their rev - els keep!

A___ home on the roll - ing deep,___Where the

scat - ter'd wa - ters rave,___And the winds their rev - els keep!___Like an

A Life on the Ocean Wave

ea – gle cag'd I pine,____ On this dull un-chang-ing shore,____ Oh!

give me the flash – ing brine,____ The spray and the tem - pest's roar,____ A

life on the o - cean wave,____ A__ home on the roll - ing deep,____ Where the

scat – ter'd wa – ters rave,____ And the winds their rev - els keep,____ The

103

A Life on the Ocean Wave

1. A life on the ocean wave!
   A home on the rolling deep!
   Where the scatter'd waters rave,
   And the winds their revels keep!
   Like an eagle cag'd I pine,
   On this dull unchanging shore,
   Oh! give me the flashing brine,
   The spray and the tempest's roar,
   A life on the ocean wave, etc.

2. Once more on the deck I stand
   Of my own swift gliding craft,
   Set sail! farewell to the land,
   The gale follows fair abaft.
   We shoot thro' the sparkling foam,
   Like an ocean-bird set free,
   Like the ocean-bird, our home
   We'll find far out on the sea!
   A life on the ocean wave, etc.

3. The land is no longer in view,
   The clouds have begun to frown,
   But with a stout vessel and crew
   We'll say, let the storm come down!
   And the song of our hearts shall be
   While the winds and waters rave,
   A life on the heaving sea!
   A home on the bounding wave!
   A life on the ocean wave, etc.

'One bright spring morning,' related Henry Russell, the composer of this song, 'as Epes Sargent strolled on the Battery, New York, watching the ships in the harbour, the scene before him gave him an idea which he proceeded to develop. His walk and song were completed together.' A pretty story, but it was, alas, a fiction. Sargent, in fact, reworked and lengthened the words of a poem by S. J. Arnold, who wrote the lyric of 'The Death of Nelson', which is printed on page 296 of this collection. Epes Sargent showed the text in 1838 to G. P. Morris, the poet, who said that it was unsuitable for musical setting. Russell asked to look at it. 'This will do, come along!' he cried, and was off to a Broadway music-store where he sat down at a piano and composed the well-known tune there and then. It was half-way to the heart of the masses at its conception: the song has a limited range, making it eminently singable, the melodic line is simple and has a very strong duple beat: utterly suitable for community rendering. Since 1889 'A Life on the Ocean Wave' has been the official march of the Royal Marines.

Epes Sargent (1813–1880), who hailed from Gloucester, Massachusetts, began his literary life early, writing a series of letters from Russia while on a journey with his father, for his school magazine. He grew to be a noted journalist, and he also wrote plays and poems. He composed anthologies for schools, and in later life devoted himself to spreading the faith of spiritualism, about which he wrote a number of books.

Henry Russell (1812–1900) was also something of a child prodigy. He was born in Sheerness, in England, and had the honour, as a boy singer at Drury Lane, of being lifted on to George IV's knee to receive a royal kiss. He studied music in Italy with Bellini, who gave him free lessons, and then worked as a pianist and chorus-master, travelling with Balfe, and also sang in opera. Having decided to seek his fortune, he crossed the Atlantic and took a job at £60 a year as organist of the First Presbyterian Church at Rochester, New York. There, he heard an oration by Henry Clay, an event, he reported later, that changed his life, determining him on the pursuit of social purpose. He began setting poems to music at this time, and left Rochester to become an itinerant singer and entertainer. He had great talents as a showman, and his performances became extremely popular. Nine years, during which he composed many famous songs, such as 'Woodman, Spare that Tree', were spent in the United States before returning to England to develop his career as a highly favoured entertainer. In later years, when inspiration flagged, he rather sadly resorted to borrowing from his former successes.

Russell thought of himself as a social reformer as much as a musician, and claimed that 'Slavery was one of the evils I helped to abolish through the medium of my songs.' His good intentions extended to such matters as temperance ('We'll quaff, we'll quaff from this cup, ha, ha! / But let the draught, but let the draught, be water, water!') and the late hours worked by shop-assistants.

Nancy Lee

Written by FRED E. WEATHERLY   Composed by STEPHEN ADAMS

1. Of all ___ the wives as e'er you know, ___ Yeo
ho! ___ lads! ho! Yeo ho! ___ yeo ___ ho! There's
none ___ like Nan - cy Lee, I trow, ___ Yeo
ho! ___ lads! ho! ___ yeo ___ ho! See,

there she stands an' waves her hands, up - on——— the quay, An'

ev' – ry day when I'm a - way she'll watch——— for me, An'

whis - per low, when tem - pests blow, for Jack——— at sea;

yeo ho!——— lads! ho!——— Yeo ho! The

sail - or's wife the sail - or's star___ shall be. Yeo

ho!___ we__ go a - cross___ the__ sea,___ The

sail - or's wife the sail - or's star___ shall be, The

sail - or's wife his star shall be.___

Nancy Lee

1. Of all the wives as e'er you know,
      Yeo ho! lads! ho! Yeo ho! yeo ho!
   There's none like Nancy Lee, I trow,
      Yeo ho! lads! ho! yeo ho!
   See, there she stands an' waves her hands, upon the quay,
   An' ev'ry day when I'm away she'll watch for me,
   An' whisper low, when tempests blow, for Jack at sea;
      Yeo ho! lads! ho! yeo ho!
      The sailor's wife the sailor's star shall be.
      Yeo ho! we go across the sea,
      The sailor's wife the sailor's star shall be,
      The sailor's wife his star shall be.

2. The harbour's past, the breezes blow,
      Yeo ho! etc.
   'Tis long ere we come back, I know,
      Yeo ho! etc.
   But true an' bright, from morn till night, my home will be,
   An' all so neat, an' snug an' sweet, for Jack at sea,
   An' Nancy's face to bless the place, an' welcome me;
      Yeo ho! etc.

3. The bo's'n pipes the watch below,
      Yeo ho! etc.
   Then here's a health afore we go,
      Yeo ho! etc.
   A long, long life to my sweet wife, an' mates at sea;
   An' keep our bones from Davy Jones, where'er we be,
   An' may you meet a mate as sweet as Nancy Lee;
      Yeo ho! etc.

This piece of yo-heave-ho of 1876 was so widely known that *Punch* was able to publish a cartoon of ten young baritones turning up at an evening party, each armed with a copy of 'Nancy Lee'. This makes ironic reading when one learns that several publishers firmly declined the song. It sold 70,000 copies in eighteen months in England alone.

Stephen Adams (1844–1913) was a composer also famous under his real name of Michael Maybrick, the baritone. He began his career as an organist, but discovering that he had a fine voice, in the words of a contemporary biographer, 'he wisely sacrificed his contrapuntal studies to devote his attention to vocal cultivation'. Sea songs were an Adams speciality: he wrote 'The Midshipmite', 'The Tar's Farewell' and 'They All Love Jack', but he also composed heroic, sentimental and sacred ballads, among them 'The Blue Alsatian Mountains'. His publisher William Boosey has described how one evening, when Maybrick had been dining rather well with the composer James Molloy (see page 63), the revellers were strolling home. Remarked Molloy, 'You have got a splendid voice, Maybrick; what a pity you waste it on those rubbishy songs of Stephen Adams.'

There are notes upon the lyricist, Fred E. Weatherly, on page 93.

The Ship I Love

Written and composed by FELIX McGLENNON

1. A gal - lant ship was lab - 'ring

Lab - 'ring in the sea;_____ The cap - tain stood a -

-mongst his crew, "Ga - ther a - round," said he._____ "This

ship is doomed and sink - ing, There on the lee is

land,_____ Then launch the boats and pull a - way, But

here at my post I'll stand._____ Good - bye, my lads, good-

- bye!_____ Good - bye, my lads, good - bye!"_____

The Ship I Love

I'll stick to the ship, lads, you save your lives,

I've no one to love me, you've chil-dren and wives;

You take to the boats, lads, pray-ing to Heav'n a-bove,

But I'll go down in the an-gry deep, with the ship I love.

D.C.

The Ship I Love

1. A gallant ship was lab'ring
       Lab'ring in the sea;
   The Captain stood amongst his crew,
       'Gather around,' said he.
   'This ship is doomed and sinking,
       There on the lee is land,
   Then launch the boats and pull away,
       But here at my post I'll stand.
   Goodbye, my lads, goodbye!'

CHORUS: I'll stick to the ship, lads,
            You save your lives,
        I've no one to love me,
            You've children and wives;
        You take to the boats, lads,
            Praying to heaven above,
        But I'll go down in the angry deep,
            With the ship I love.

2. The crew stood hesitating,
       Their hearts were staunch and true;
   With tear-dimm'd eyes spoke up the mate,
       'Sir, we will die with you!'
   The Captain cried, 'What? Mutiny?
       I am the captain here!
   So launch the boats and pull away,
       And think of your children dear.
   Goodbye, my lads, goodbye!'

CHORUS: I'll stick to the ship, lads, etc.

Introduced to music-hall audiences by the celebrated Tom Costello, 'The Ship I Love' belongs in spirit to the parlour vocalist, and is one of the few examples of music-hall songs that appealed to the sedate middle class. The catchy, perky little tune is not entirely in accord with either the tragedy or the captain's noble resolve. Its origins show in the feeling one gets, as bar by bar the melody proceeds, that it will end in a convulsing laugh-line—which never comes. Some details of the author and composer are to be found on page 68.

Far & Wide

or, Songs of Foreign Lands

The Irish Emigrant

Written by LADY DUFFERIN

Composed by GEORGE BARKER

Andante

mf

ritard.

Joyously

1. I'm sit-ting on the stile Ma-ry, where we sat side by side On a

bright May morn-ing long a-go, when first you were my bride; The

p

corn was spring-ing fresh and green and the lark sang loud and high, And the

The Irish Emigrant

red was on your lip Ma-ry, and the love-light in your eye.

2. The place is lit-tle chang'd Ma-ry, the day is bright as then; The

lark's loud song is in my ear and the corn is green a-gain; But I

miss the soft clasp of your hand, and your breath, warm on my cheek; And I

still keep list'-ning for the words you ne-ver more will speak, you

ne-ver more will speak. —

Slower

3. I'm ve – ry lone – ly now Ma-ry, for the poor make no new friends; But

oh, they love the bet-ter still the few our Fa – ther sends! And

you were all I have Ma – ry my bless-ing and my pride: There's

no – thing left to care for now since my poor Ma – ry died. —

The Irish Emigrant

Slower

4. I'm bid-ding you a long fare-well my Ma - ry, kind and true! But I'll not for-get you dar - ling, in the land I'm go-ing to; They say there's bread and work for all, and the sun shines al-ways there; But I'll not for-get old Ire - land, were it fif - ty times as fair, were it fif - ty times as fair.

119

The Irish Emigrant

1. I'm sitting on the stile Mary, where we sat side by side
   On a bright May morning long ago, when first you were my bride;
   The corn was springing fresh and green and the lark sang loud and high,
   And the red was on your lip Mary, and the lovelight in your eye.

2. The place is little chang'd Mary, the day is bright as then;
   The lark's loud song is in my ear and the corn is green again;
   But I miss the soft clasp of your hand, and your breath, warm on my cheek;
   And I still keep list'ning for the words you never more will speak,
       You never more will speak.

3. I'm very lonely now Mary, for the poor make no new friends;
   But oh, they love the better still the few our Father sends!
   And you were all I had Mary—my blessing and my pride:
   There's nothing left to care for now since my poor Mary died.

4. I'm bidding you a long farewell my Mary, kind and true!
   But I'll not forget you darling, in the land I'm going to;
   They say there's bread and work for all, and the sun shines always there;
   But I'll not forget old Ireland, were it fifty times as fair,
       Were it fifty times as fair.

Frederick Temple Hamilton Blackwood, Lord Dufferin and Ava, was a distinguished diplomat who served as Governor-General of Canada and India and as Her Brittanic Majesty's Ambassador to Russia, Turkey, Italy and France. He wrote *Irish Emigration and the Tenure of Land in Ireland*, and it was his devoted work for that unhappy country that suggested to his wife the theme for this song. It should not be confused with another extremely popular ballad, 'The Lament of the Irish Emigrant' by William R. Dempster and Mrs Price Blackwood.

The poetess, Helen Selina Sheridan, Lady Dufferin (1807–1867) was the grand-daughter of the dramatist, Richard Brinsley Sheridan, and sister of the fiery Caroline, the Hon. Mrs Norton, who wrote 'The Arab's Farewell to His Steed' and 'Juanita'. Lady Dufferin published her songs anonymously, as befitted a member of the aristocracy, and wrote a play, the authorship of which she did not acknowledge.

George Barker (1812–1876) was a tenor singer who also composed songs. His 'White Squall' was his most successful and it retained favour all through the century. 'The Irish Emigrant' has a simple, pleasant ballad feel about it, and should be sung fluidly to cope with the sometimes haphazard word-setting.

I'll Take You Home Again, Kathleen

Written and composed by THOMAS P. WESTENDORF

Andante con espressione

With feeling

1. I'll take you home a-gain, Kath-leen, A - cross the o-cean wild and wide, To where your heart has ev - er been, Since first you were my bon-ny bride. The ro - ses all have left your

cheek,   I've watch'd   them fade a - way and   die;   Your

voice   is sad when e'er you speak,   And   tears   be-dim your lov-ing eyes.

CHORUS

Oh!   I   will   take you back, Kath - leen,   To

Oh!   Take you back, Kath-leen,

Oh!   Take you back, Kath-leen,

Oh!   Take you back, Kath-leen,

I'll Take You Home Again, Kathleen

where your heart will feel no pain, And when the fields are fresh and

Heart will feel no pain,

Heart will feel no pain,

Heart will feel no pain,

green, I'll__ take you to your home a - gain._____

Fields are fresh and green, Take you to your home a - gain, home a - gain.

Fields are fresh and green, Take you to your home a - gain, home a - gain.

Fields are fresh and green, Take you to your home a - gain. home a - gain.

I'll Take You Home Again, Kathleen

1. I'll take you home again, Kathleen,
     Across the ocean wild and wide,
   To where your heart has ever been,
     Since first you were my bonny bride.
   The roses all have left your cheek,
     I've watch'd them fade away and die;
   Your voice is sad whene'er you speak,
     And tears bedim your loving eyes.

CHORUS: Oh, I will take you back, Kathleen,
             To where your heart will feel no pain,
             And when the fields are fresh and green,
             I'll take you to your home again.

2. I know you love me, Kathleen, dear,
     Your heart was ever fond and true;
   I always feel when you are near,
     That life holds nothing dear but you.
   The smiles that once you gave to me,
     I scarcely ever see them now,
   Though many, many times I see,
     A dark'ning shadow on your brow.

CHORUS: Oh, I will take you back, Kathleen, etc.

3. To that dear home beyond the sea,
     My Kathleen shall again return,
   And when thy old friends welcome thee,
     Thy loving heart will cease to yearn.
   Where laughs the little silver stream,
     Beside your mother's humble cot,
   And brightest rays of sunshine gleam,
     There all your grief will be forgot.

CHORUS: Oh, I will take you back, Kathleen, etc.

Although definitely American, this song was adopted by the Irish immigrants as their own. The composer came from Virginia and he wrote this plaintive ballad at Plainfield, Indiana. The traditional story of Mrs Westendorf's incurable illness and grief at her son's death has been proved fictitious. In fact, Thomas Paine Westendorf (1848–1923) and his wife were temporarily separated soon after their marriage when she went to stay with her parents in New York while her husband was teaching at Plainfield. The song was written in 1875 in reply to another currently popular, 'Barney, Take Me Home Again'. Mrs Westendorf's real name was not Kathleen, but Jennie.

The Miner's Dream of Home

Written and composed by WILL GODWIN and LEO DRYDEN

1. It is ten wea - ry years since I left Eng - land's shore, In a far dis - tant coun - try to roam,_____ How I long to re - turn to my own na - tive

land,   To my friends and the   old folks at   home!_____ Last

night, as   I   slum-bered, I   had   a strange dream, One that seemed to   bring

p sostenuto

dis-tant friends   near,_____   I   dreamt of Old   Eng-land, the

land   of my   birth,   To the heart of her   sons ev - er   dear._____

rit.

CHORUS *Legato*

I   saw the old   home-stead and   fa - ces I   love,   I   saw Eng-land's

The Miner's Dream of Home

val - leys and dells,_____ I lis-ten'd with joy, as I did when a

boy, To the sound of the old vil - lage bells._____ The log was

burn - ing bright-ly,_____ 'Twas a night that should ban - ish all sin,_____

_ For the bells were ring - ing the old year out, And the

new year in. 1. I in._____ 2.

The Miner's Dream of Home

1. It is ten weary years since I left England's shore,
   In a far distant country to roam,
   How I long to return to my own native land,
   To my friends and the old folks at home!
   Last night, as I slumbered, I had a strange dream,
   One that seemed to bring distant friends near,
   I dreamt of Old England, the land of my birth,
   To the heart of her sons ever dear.

CHORUS: I saw the old homestead and faces I love,
   I saw England's valleys and dells,
   I listen'd with joy, as I did when a boy,
   To the sound of the old village bells.
   The log was burning brightly,
   'Twas a night that should banish all sin,
   For the bells were ringing the old year out,
   And the new year in.

2. While the joyous bells rang, swift I wended my way
   To the cot where I lived when a boy;
   And I looked in the window, Yes! there by the fire,
   Sat my parents! my heart filled with joy.
   The tears trickled fast down my bronzed, furrowed cheek
   As I gazed on my mother so dear,
   I knew in my heart she was raising a prayer
   For the boy whom she dreamt not was near!

CHORUS: I saw the old homestead and faces I love, etc.

3. At the door of the cottage we met face to face,
   'Twas the first time for ten weary years;
   Soon the past was forgotten, we stood hand in hand,
   Father, mother, and wand'rer in tears!
   Once more in the fireplace the oak log burns bright,
   And I promised no more would I roam;
   As I sat in the old vacant chair by the hearth,
   And I sang the dear song 'Home, Sweet Home!'

CHORUS: I saw the old homestead and faces I love, etc.

Although the origin of this song lies in the music-hall in 1891, the ballad had great currency in lower middle-class parlours. Leo Dryden (died 1939), 'the Kipling of the halls', was famous for his performances of patriotic sketches and songs, hymning the British Empire and its thin red line: 'Bravo, Dublin Fusiliers', 'The Gallant Gordon Highlanders' and 'The Great White Mother', which he rendered against a projected magic-lantern slide of Queen Victoria. In later years Dryden was reduced to destitution, and was found singing 'The Miner's Dream of Home' in the streets.

Will Godwin (died 1913) is also known as the author of such works for the stage as 'Hi diddle diddle um' and 'Beer, Beer, Glorious Beer'.

It is not only the subject-matter that has made 'The Miner's Dream' so perennially popular: it has a timeless melody that swings beautifully into the waltz-like chorus.

I'll Sing Thee Songs of Araby

Written by W. G. WILLS

Composed by FREDERICK CLAY

129

rain - bow vi - sions rise,___ And all my soul___ shall strive to wake Sweet

won - der in___ thine eyes,___ And all my soul shall strive to wake Sweet

won - der in thine eyes!___

2. Through those twin lakes, when won-der wakes,___ My

rap - tur'd song shall sink,___ And as the di - ver dives___ for___ pearls,___ Bring

I'll Sing Thee Songs of Araby

tears, bright tears to their brink;___ And dreams of de-light shall on thee break,___ And

rain - bow vi - sions rise,___ And all my soul___ shall strive to wake Sweet

won - der in___ thine eyes,___ And all my soul shall strive to wake Sweet

won - der in thine eyes, To cheat thee of a sigh___ Or

charm thee to a tear!

I'll Sing Thee Songs of Araby

1. I'll sing thee songs of Araby,
   And tales of fair Cashmere,
Wild tales to cheat thee of a sigh,
   Or charm thee to a tear.
And dreams of delight shall on thee break,
   And rainbow visions rise,
And all my soul shall strive to wake
   Sweet wonder in thine eyes!

2. Through those twin lakes, when wonder wakes,
   My raptur'd song shall sink,
And as the diver dives for pearls,
   Bring tears, bright tears to their brink;
And dreams of delight shall on thee break,
   And rainbow visions rise,
And all my soul shall strive to wake
   Sweet wonder in thine eyes,
To cheat thee of a sigh
   Or charm thee to a tear!

This seemingly imperishable song has been the favourite of many famous tenors from Sims Reeves onwards.

W. G. Wills (1828–1891) failed to take a degree at Trinity College, Dublin, and spent most of his early manhood in a riotous form of what he called 'daisy picking'. What his father called it is not recorded. Settling in London, he found writing for magazines and the stage modestly lucrative, and he also set up a studio as a portrait painter. An avowed Bohemian, living, by all accounts in picturesque filth surrounded by stray cats, monkeys and other 'unclean animals' (*Dictionary of National Biography*), he felt himself too unconventional to paint a portrait of the royal grandchildren when invited to do so. Later, he retired almost permanently to bed to write, and he provided Sir Henry Irving with, among other dramas, *Charles I*. From then on he churned out large quantities of poor plays. From a distance he looked like a genius, but that impression did not bear closer inspection.

The composer, Frederic Clay (1840–1889), was the son of the English Member of Parliament and whist-player, James Clay. He worked for a time in the Treasury, but became a composer for the stage, providing music for some fifteen operas and plays. He also wrote two cantatas, and in one of them, *Lalla Rookh*, this ballad is to be found. Clay was a fine melodist, capable of great tenderness, as shown by such songs as 'She Wandered down the Mountain Side' and 'The Sands of Dee'. 'I'll Sing Thee Songs of Araby' is a fine strophic setting. Notice the return of the introductory piano motif for the coda and also the serene effect of the pronounced third in the final tonic chord.

A Son of the Desert am I

Written by JOHN P. WILSON

Composed by WALTER A. PHILLIPS

1. A son of the des-ert am I, _____ The i - ron clad hoofs of my horse spurn the sand. The wide spread-ing des - ert is peace - ful and grand; My

good lance at rest, at my side hangs my brand. My brave A-rab com-rades come at my com-mand.

For a son of the des-ert am I ____ None so daunt-less and free on ____ land or on sea, For a son of the de-sert am I, ____ None so

A Son of the Desert am I

daunt - less and free on land or on sea, For a son of the de - sert am

I____

Allegro

p

RECIT.

2. I scoff at the Sy - bar-ite's case so se - cure, Lux-

accel.

- u - ri - ous life I could nev-er en-dure: 'Tis free - dom I love, though the

grandioso

world be ob-scure. The des-ert's wild grandeur a - lone can al-lure, For a

son of the des-ert am I._____ None so

3. And I know_____ that Zu - li - ca a - waits_____ in her

tent,_____ The fair - est in all_____ the sun - kiss'd_____ O - ri -

- ent;_____ Whose form_____ has the grace_____ of the palm_____ hea-ven-

A Son of the Desert am I

- sent,___ She will wel - come her love ___ when the storm-cloud is spent,__

f **Allegretto**

For a son of the des-ert am I,_____ For a son of the des-ert am

f **Tempo di marcia**

I_____ None so daunt - less and free on__ land or on sea, For a

son of the des-ert am I _____ None so daunt - less and free on

land or on sea, For a son of the des - ert am I._____

A Son of the Desert am I

1. A son of the desert am I,
   The iron clad hoofs of my horse spurn the sand.
   The wide spreading desert is peaceful and grand;
   My good lance at rest, at my side hangs my brand.
   My brave Arab comrades come at my command.
   For a son of the desert am I.

   None so dauntless and free on land or on sea,
   For a son of the desert am I,
   None so dauntless and free on land or on sea,
   For a son of the desert am I.

2. I scoff at the Sybarite's ease so secure,
   Luxurious life I could never endure:
   'Tis freedom I love, though the world be obscure.
   The desert's wild grandeur alone can allure,
   For a son of the desert am I.

   None so dauntless and free, etc.

3. And I know that Zulica awaits in her tent,
   The fairest in all the sun-kiss'd orient;
   Whose form has the grace of the palm heaven-sent,
   She will welcome her love when the storm-cloud is spent,
   For a son of the desert am I.

   None so dauntless and free, etc.

Given a baritone who can perform with real bravura and, for the third stanza, dulcet tenderness, this piece can still have an electric effect upon its audience. Whatever its actual origins, which the present editor has not been able to uncover, this is one of the most operatically conceived of all the songs in this collection.

Hearth & Home

or, Songs of the Family

Home! Sweet Home!

Written by JOHN HOWARD PAYNE   Composed by SIR HENRY BISHOP

1. 'Mid pleas - ures and Pa - la-ces though we may roam, Be it

e - ver so hum - ble there's no place like home! A

Home! Sweet Home!

charm___ from the skies seems to hal - low us there,___ Which

seek___ through the world, is ne'er met with else - where.

espress.

Home! Home,___ sweet sweet Home! There's no___ place like

Largo *tr* **Tempo Imo**

Home!___ There's no___ place like Home!___

colla voce *pp* *ff* *ten.*

più animato

2. An Ex - ile from Home, Splen-dour

141

Home! Sweet Home!

1. 'Mid pleasures and Palaces though we may roam,
   Be it ever so humble there's no place like home!
   A charm from the skies seems to hallow us there,
   Which seek through the world, is ne'er met with elsewhere.
      Home! Home, sweet sweet Home!
   There's no place like Home! There's no place like Home!

2. An Exile from Home, Splendour dazzles in vain!
   Oh! give me my lowly thatch'd Cottage again!
   The Birds singing gaily that came at my call,
   Give me them with the peace of mind dearer than all!
      Home! Home, sweet sweet Home!
   There's no place like Home! There's no place like Home!

The most famous song in this collection 'has done more than statesmanship or legislation to keep alive in the hearts of the people the virtues that flourish at the fireside, and to recall to its hallowed circle the wanderers who stray from it'. Thus Dr Charles Mackay, the Victorian poet, journalist and song-writer. Ever since it charmed its first audience on May 8th, 1823, at the première of the melodrama, *Clari; or, the Maid of Milan*, it has been an undying favourite at the fireside and on the concert platform the world over. Jenny Lind sang it in Washington when the author was in the audience causing 'a whirlwind of excitement and enthusiasm'; Antoinette Sterling sang it at Henry Ward Beecher's church, and an old man came to her afterwards and handed her two unpublished verses entrusted to him by Payne; Malibran was forced by an ecstatic audience to interpolate it in the middle of an opera in New York; Adelina Patti sang it in London at the audition that marked the beginning of her brilliant career; Marie Albani claimed she had sung it more times than any other singer in all parts of the globe—at Kimberley in South Africa she performed it for a group of Zulus who 'applauded in a dignified manner, and then walked solemnly away'.

John Howard Payne (1791–1852) was an American actor who led a chequered career: he had a modest success as a boy prodigy in New York and subsequently in England, but he had to keep body and soul together by translating French melodramas for the London stage. Edmund Kean and Charles Kemble both appeared in his plays. *Clari*, the story of a virtuous peasant maid abducted by a wicked duke, contained only six musical numbers, all composed by Henry Bishop. The origin of the melody of 'Home! Sweet Home!' has been the subject of long dispute, but Bishop himself told Dr Mackay that when young he had the commission of editing a collection of national airs of all countries, and having no Sicilian melody to include invented one, to words by Thomas Haynes Bayly, 'To the Home of My Childhood'. After the success of the song in *Clari*, when pirates were busy reprinting the piece believing it to be genuinely Sicilian, Bishop swore evidence that he was the sole composer. Another version of the origin of the melody makes it a genuine peasant song, a Calabrian tune handed down by the mountain folk of Sicily, transmitted to Bishop by a certain Captain Alexander, who had served on that island. Certainly, 'Home! Sweet Home!' is not the traditional eighteenth-century *siciliano*, which was in slow dance form in 6/8 or sometimes 12/8, usually in a minor key.

Sir Henry Rowley Bishop (1786–1855) made his mark with music for such melodramas and operas as *The Circassian Bride*, *The Maniac*, *The Miller and his Men* and

Guy Mannering. He later became a figure of apparent respectability, Professor of Music at Edinburgh, Heather Professor of Music at Oxford, and the first professional musician to be knighted. He composed many exceedingly popular songs—another of them, 'My Pretty Jane', is in this volume. 'Home! Sweet Home!' does not truly represent Sir Henry's character; he was a noted reprobate, home-wrecker and spendthrift, and died in poverty.

Money had a habit of running through Payne's fingers, also; he sold *Clari* for an outright fee of £250 and his name did not even appear on the published sheet music of 'Home! Sweet Home!' The irony of Payne's authorship of the song struck him keenly. He never had a home of his own, and, after his death, the following poignant note was found in his diary:

> How often have I been in the heart of Paris, Berlin, London or some other city, and have heard persons singing or hand-organs playing 'Home! Sweet Home!', without having a shilling to buy myself the next meal, or a place to lay my head. The world has literally sung my song until every heart is familiar with its melody, yet I have been a wanderer from my boyhood.

He was a wanderer to the last, dying as American consul in Tunis.

As performed in the opera, the song comprised only the two stanzas reproduced above. Three others are reprinted in *Parlour Poetry* and this editor knows of at least four more of dubious origin and doubtful quality. Most of the controversy about the song has centred on the provenance of the music, but the words may not be entirely the result of the poetic inspiration which descended upon Payne in a Paris garret, as he sat lonely and penniless while the sounds of the happy, careless throng welled up from the boulevard below. The famous verses may have come to him 'as spontaneously as a sigh', but in 1796 in the *Gentleman's Magazine* appeared a translation of the old Latin song, 'Dulce Domum', one line of which runs:

> Home, sweet home! an ample treasure

and in 1818, the American J. K. Paulding published his poem *The Backwoodsman*, which contained the lines:

> Whate'er may happen, whereso'er we roam,
> However homely, still there's naught like home.

Whatever the antecedents of the song, whatever its literary and musical qualities (both the subject of frequent critical scorn over the years), it certainly struck as no other composition has done a responsive chord in the human breast. Perhaps its timeless appeal is due in part to the restrained quality of the melodic writing; there is, to use a contemporary term, no real 'gut' in the tune at all, and it meanders back to the tonic, giving the impression that it never really left there at all. This is, one may hazard, a vacuum of a tune which nostalgia rushes to fill. There is just enough melody to support but not dominate the yearning of the words.

It must be one of the few songs that have had a song written to celebrate it: Julian Jordan's piece, 'The Song That Reached My Heart', achieved great acclaim a century ago:

> She sang a song, a song of home,
>   A song that reach'd my heart.
> Home, home, sweet, sweet home.
> She sang the song of 'Home, Sweet Home',
>   The song that reach'd my heart.

Two final, slightly macabre notes. 'Home! Sweet Home!' was a melody forbidden to calliopes, the steam pianos of the Mississippi show-boats, for superstition had it that the vessel playing the tune would end up on the bottom of the river before the next sunset. Dr Percy Scholes, the English musicologist, has noted that an Oklahoma newspaper reported in 1935 that 'Home! Sweet Home!' was sung in court by an attorney to beg mercy for his bank-robber client. The jury promptly brought in a sentence of life imprisonment.

Woodman, Spare That Tree

Written by G. P. Morris Composed by Henry Russell

146

Woodman, Spare That Tree

1. Wood – man spare that tree!_____ Touch not a sin – gle__ bough; In youth it shel – ter'd me,_____ And__ I'll pro-tect it now; 'Twas my fore fa – ther's__ hand_____ That placed it near his cot, There,

woodman, let____ it stand,_____ Thy_ axe shall harm____ it

not!

That old fa - mi - liar tree,_____ Whose glo - ry and_ re -

-nown Are spread o'er land and sea,_____ And_

Woodman, Spare That Tree

1. Woodman, spare that tree!
   Touch not a single bough;
   In youth it shelter'd me,
   And I'll protect it now;
   'Twas my forefather's hand
   That placed it near his cot,
   There, woodman, let it stand,
   Thy axe shall harm it not!
   That old familiar tree,
   Whose glory and renown
   Are spread o'er land and sea,
   And wouldst thou hew it down?
   Woodman, forbear thy stroke!
   Cut not its earth-bound ties;
   Oh! spare that aged oak
   Now tow'ring to the skies!

2. When but an idle boy
   I sought its grateful shade;
   In all their gushing joy
   Here, too, my sisters played.
   My Mother kiss'd me here;
   My Father press'd my hand—
   Forgive this foolish tear,
   But let that old oak stand!
   My heart-strings round thee cling,
   Close as thy bark, old friend!
   Here shall the wild-bird sing
   And still thy branches bend,
   Old tree, the storm still brave!
   And, woodman, leave the spot;
   While I've a hand to save,
   Thy axe shall harm it not.

Henry Russell, the composer, and G. P. Morris, the poet, had occasion to visit the latter's old homestead near Bloomingdale, New York, where there was a fine old tree planted by the latter's grandfather. In Russell's own words:

> As we neared the homely cottage which had once housed the Morris family, my friend noticed an old man with his coat off, sharpening an axe.
> 'What are you going to do?' asked the poet with a tremor of apprehension in his tone. 'You surely do not intend to cut down that tree?'
> 'Yes, sirree,' was the blunt reply.

The old man wanted firewood, so Morris paid him $10, the tree's worth, 'and the daughter of the woodman pledged her word that the tree should stand as long as she lived'. Russell suggested to Morris that he commemorate the event in poetry, which he did, and his friend provided the musical setting. The song was an instant success in the United States in 1837 and also, shortly afterwards, in Britain. Russell has also told the story of how he was once singing in the north of England. After the end of his rendering of 'Woodman, Spare That Tree', an old man in the audience stood up to demand earnestly, 'Was the tree spared, sir?' 'It was,' said Russell. The man sighed with relief. 'Thank God for that,' he replied. Other versions of the story set it in various towns on both sides of the Atlantic.

Russell also passed on another anecdote that illustrates how musical taste was likely to be formed in the last century:

> A very dear friend of mine, now well-known as a public man ... has often told me that he dates the birth of his sentimental nature to the fact that an old nurse used to sing 'Woodman, Spare That Tree' at his bedside, and that scores of times as a child he cried himself to sleep over the simple song.

Many parodies also celebrate this ballad. One of them of 1868 was written when he was a student by John Love, Jr, of New York University. It is entitled 'Barber, Spare Those Hairs', and one verse runs:

Woodman, Spare That Tree

O barber, spare those hairs,
Which sprout from both my cheeks,
A solace for my cares;
I've cherished them for weeks.
They come in single file,
As though afraid to bloom;
But still they're all the style,
So barber, give them room.

The title of the song was originally 'The Old Oak Tree', with an illustration upon the sheet music of a woodman with an axe obviously sadly inadequate for the task that confronts him—an elephantine oak, with a trunk at least six feet across. Russell was addicted to the word 'old', for he wrote such ballads as 'The Old Arm Chair', 'The Brave Old Oak', 'The Old Sexton' and 'The Old Bell'. There are some notes upon Henry Russell on page 105.

General George Pope Morris (1802–1864) came from Philadelphia to begin his career in a New York printing office. He was soon writing verses for the press, and at the age of twenty-one founded the *New York Mirror*, a weekly that published the literary notabilities of the day. Morris was a playwright as well as journalist and poet, and one of the Knickerbocker School, a metropolitan group of writers who were very conscious of their role as the founders of American literature.

Ben Bolt

Written by THOMAS DUNN ENGLISH **Composed by NELSON KNEASS**

1. Oh! don't you re-mem-ber sweet A-lice, Ben Bolt - Sweet A-lice with hair____ so brown?. She

Ben Bolt

153

gran - ite so gray, And sweet A - lice lies un - der the stone.

2. Oh! don't you re-mem -ber the wood, Ben Bolt, Near the

green sun -ny slope of the hill; Where oft we have sung 'neath its

wide— spread -ing shade, And kept time to the click of the

Ben Bolt

mill? The mill has gone to de - cay, Ben Bolt, And a
qui - et now reigns all a - round, See the
old___ rus - tic porch, with its ros - es so sweet, Lies___
scat - ter'd and fal - len to the ground. See the
old___ rus - tic porch, with its ros - es so sweet, Lies___

155

scat -ter'd and fal -len to the ground,

ad lib.

a tempo

3. Oh! don't you re-mem-ber the

p

school, Ben Bolt, And the Mas -ter so kind and so true, And the

lit -tle nook by the clear___ run -ning brook, Where we

gath -er'd the flow'rs as they grew? On the Mas - ter's grave grows the

Ben Bolt

grass, Ben Bolt, And the run-ning lit-tle brook is now dry; And of all __ the friends who were school_ mates then, There re-main, Ben, but you ____ and I! And of all __ the friends who were school_ mates then, There re-main, Ben, but you ____ and I.

ad lib.

ad lib.

Ben Bolt

1. Oh! don't you remember sweet Alice, Ben Bolt—
   Sweet Alice with hair so brown?
   She wept with delight when you gave her a smile,
   And trembled with fear at your frown.
   In the old church yard, in the valley, Ben Bolt,
   In a corner obscure and alone,
   They have fitted a slab of granite so gray,
   And sweet Alice lies under the stone.

2. Oh! don't you remember the wood, Ben Bolt,
   Near the green sunny slope of the hill;
   Where oft we have sung 'neath its wide spreading shade,
   And kept time to the click of the mill?
   The mill has gone to decay, Ben Bolt,
   And a quiet now reigns all around,
   See the old rustic porch, with its roses so sweet,
   Lies scatter'd and fallen to the ground,

3. Oh! don't you remember the school, Ben Bolt,
   And the Master so kind and so true,
   And the little nook by the clear running brook,
   Where we gather'd the flow'rs as they grew?
   On the Master's grave grows the grass, Ben Bolt,
   And the running little brook is now dry;
   And of all the friends who were schoolmates then,
   There remain, Ben, but you and I!

It is instructive to compare this lyric, so straightforwardly sentimental, with the significantly more muscular poem as originally written by Thomas Dunn English. The first stanza is much the same, give or take a few syllables, but then the texts diverge. Here is the fourth verse to compare to the last verse, above:

And don't you remember the school, Ben Bolt,
   With the master so cruel and grim,
And the shaded nook in the running brook
   Where the children went to swim? . . .

And so on. The schoolmaster's nature suffered an unlikely amelioration during the composition of the song, and the song's publisher insisted that the line 'Where the children used to swim' be changed as it offended against propriety. No wonder Dr English was inclined to disown the song in later years. The composer, or rather arranger, for he adapted an old German tune, set a mutilated version and the original poet was never paid a penny for his inspiration.

The song, which dates from 1848, was immensely popular for more than half a century, receiving a new lease of life in the 'nineties when the evil Svengali forced the heroine Trilby, in the melodrama of the same name, into singing it under hypnotic trance. It is often described as a sea song: the only nautical reference occurs in the final stanza of the original poem:

Ben Bolt

There is change in the things I loved, Ben Bolt,
   They have changed from the old to the new;
But I feel in the deeps of my spirit the truth,
   There never was change in you.
Twelve months twenty have passed, Ben Bolt,
   Since first we were friends—yet I hail
Your presence a blessing, your friendship a truth,
   Ben Bolt of the salt-sea gale.

Dr Thomas Dunn English (1819–1902) was a doctor, lawyer, politician, journalist, playwright and poet who lived at Newark, New Jersey. He once had a violent quarrel with Edgar Allan Poe, whom he accused publicly of forgery, and received a thrashing at Poe's hands for his pains.

Not a lot is known of Nelson Kneass. He was, when he set 'Ben Bolt' to music, a black-face Minstrel at the Eagle Ice Cream Saloon in Pittsburgh. On one occasion, when musical director of the Saloon, he heard the song 'Away Down Souf', by a young book-keeper called Stephen Foster, and was so struck by it that he tried to establish copyright for it the next day—in his own name.

Rock Me to Sleep

Written by ELIZABETH AKERS ALLEN   Composed by SIR JULIUS BENEDICT

1. Back-ward, turn back-ward, oh Time in your flight! Make me a child a-gain, just for to-night! Mo-ther come back from the e-cho-less shore, Take me a-gain to your

Rock Me to Sleep

the sil – ver threads out

of my hair, O - ver my slum-bers your

lov - ing watch keep; O - ver my slum-bers your lov - ing watch

keep; Rock me to sleep rock me to sleep

Rock Me to Sleep

Rock Me to Sleep

1. Backward, turn backward, oh Time in your flight!
   Make me a child again, just for tonight!
   Mother come back from the echoless shore,
   Take me again to your heart, as of yore.
   Kiss from my forehead the furrows of care,
   Smooth the silver threads out of my hair,
   Over my slumbers your loving watch keep;
   Rock me to sleep, Mother, rock me to sleep.

2. Mother, dear Mother! the years have been long,
   Since I last hush'd to your lullaby song;
   Yet with strong yearnings and passionate pain,
   Long I tonight for your presence again.
   Sick of the hollow, the base, the untrue,
   Mother, dear Mother, my heart calls for you!
   Never hereafter to wake or to weep;
   Rock me to sleep, Mother, rock me to sleep.

Like 'Ben Bolt', this song was adapted rather drastically from the original poem. The second stanza is a patchwork from the sixth verse of the original plus a few lines from other verses. The full text may be consulted in *Parlour Poetry*. The song was first published under Mrs Allen's pen name of Florence Percy. There is also another setting by Ernest Leslie, and a number of parodies. Here is a snatch from a recent one, a cowboy song:

Backward, turn backward, film guy in your flight,
And turn out a cowboy that does the game right.
Put on a picture that won't look so strange
To us old punchers who've rode on the range.

Elizabeth Akers Allen (1832–1911) was a lady journalist of some note who also wrote poetry and novels. She married twice and used a variety of names to head her pieces. For a time she was a newspaper editor in Portland, Maine.

The father of Sir Julius Benedict (1804–1885) was a Jewish banker in Stuttgart. Young Julius studied music under Weber and began his career on the Continent, but settled in England in 1835 to become one of the country's greatest conductors of opera and oratorio. His talents were approved at the most distinguished levels, and he received, among many other honours, knighthoods from the rulers of Austria and Württemberg as well as Britain. He toured the United States as Jenny Lind's concert director. Of the many operas, oratorios and cantatas he wrote only one is remembered now, *The Lily of Killarney*. 'Rock Me to Sleep' is more adventurous harmonically than much of Benedict and can even today be extremely effective in performance. For many years Benedict conducted the Monday Popular Concerts at St James's Hall, and so regularly did he promote his own annual concert in London—for over forty years—that he was nicknamed 'Sir Jubilee Benefit'.

Grandfather's Clock

Written and composed by HENRY CLAY WORK

1. My grand-fa-ther's clock was too large for the shelf, So it stood nine-ty years on the floor; It was tal-ler by half than the old man him self, Though it weigh'd not a pen-ny-weight more. It was

bought on the morn of the day that he was born, And was

al - ways his trea - sure and pride; But it stopp'd short

ne - ver to go a - gain When the old man died.

In exact time

Nine - ty years with - out slum - ber - ing (tick, tock, tick, tock), His

Nine - ty years with - out slum - ber - ing (tick, tock, tick, tock), His

Nine - ty years with - out slum - ber - ing (tick, tock, tick, tock), His

Nine - ty years with - out slum - ber - ing His

Grandfather's Clock

life — se - conds number-ing (tick, tock, tick, tock), It stopp'd short

life — se - conds number-ing (tick, tock, tick, tock), It stopp'd short

life — se - conds number-ing (tick, tock, tick, tock), It stopp'd short

life — se - conds number-ing It stopp'd short

ne-ver to go a - gain When the old man died.

ne-ver to go a - gain When the old man died.

ne-ver to go a - gain When the old man died.

ne-ver to go a - gain When the old man died.

Grandfather's Clock

1. My grandfather's clock was too large for the shelf,
   So it stood ninety years on the floor;
   It was taller by half than the old man himself,
   Though it weigh'd not a pennyweight more.
   It was bought on the morn of the day that he was born,
   And was always his treasure and pride;
       But it stopp'd short—never to go again—
       When the old man died.

CHORUS: Ninety years without slumbering
           (tick, tock, tick, tock),
       His life-seconds numbering
           (tick, tock, tick, tock),
       It stopp'd short—never to go again—
       When the old man died.

2. In watching its pendulum swing to and fro,
   Many hours had he spent while a boy;
   And in childhood and manhood the clock seem'd to know
   And to share both his grief and his joy.
   For it struck twenty four when he enter'd at the door,
   With a blooming and beautiful bride;
       But it stopp'd short—never to go again—
       When the old man died.

CHORUS: Ninety years without slumbering, etc.

3. My grandfather said that of those he could hire,
   Not a servant so faithful he found;
   For it wasted no time and had but one desire—
   At the close of each week to be wound.
   And it kept in its place—not a frown upon its face,
   And its hands never hung by its side;
       But it stopp'd short—never to go again—
       When the old man died.

CHORUS: Ninety years without slumbering, etc.

4. It rang an alarm in the dead of the night,
   An alarm that for years had been dumb;
   And we knew that his spirit was pluming for flight—
   That his hour of departure had come.
   Still the clock kept the time, with a soft and muffled chime,
   As we silently stood by its side;
       But it stopp'd short—never to go again—
       When the old man died.

CHORUS: Ninety years without slumbering, etc.

The domestic clock provided as much inspiration to Victorian poets as did the old armchair. Longfellow was so impressed by a clock belonging to some of his wife's relatives that he wrote a poem, 'The Old Clock on the Stairs', which had great popularity as a song. Charles Swain, a now forgotten bard who was very celebrated in his time, wrote 'The Old Cottage Clock' which James L. Molloy set to music:

> Tick, tick, it said,
> To the churchyard bed,
> The grave hath given warning,
> Up, up and rise, and look to the skies,
> And prepare for a heavenly morning.

In some early editions of 'Grandfather's Clock', its voice is not a measured 'tick, tock', but a frenetic 'tick, tick'. This really is a timeless song with an excellent chorus and an easy melodic line. One should relish the skilful use of quavers at 'stopped, short'.

Henry Clay Work (1832–1884) was an abolitionist, Unionist and prohibitionist printer from Connecticut who was so skilled at setting music type that he is said to have composed melodies directly in lead. Something of a mechanical genius, as well as a composer, he was an inventor of machines and toys. Self-taught as a musician, he had a remarkable melodic gift and was able to express his fervent political views in such famous songs as 'Kingdom Coming' or 'The Year of Jubilo', and 'Marching through Georgia', which is still unappreciated in the South. The temperance strain shows in 'Come Home, Father' (page 246), and this volume contains two more ballads by Work, rather less known, 'Watching for Pa' (page 180) and 'Ring the Bell, Watchman' (page 222).

A Boy's Best Friend is His Mother

Written by HENRY MILLER

Composed by JOSEPH P. SKELLY

1. While plod-ding on our way, the toil-some road of life, How few the friends that dai-ly there we meet! Not ma-ny will stand by in trou-ble and in strife, With

A Boy's Best Friend is His Mother

coun – sel and af – fec – tion ev – er sweet!_____ But

there is one whose smile, will ev – er on us beam, Whose

love is dear – er far than an – y o – ther_____ And where-

- ev – er we may turn, This les – son we will learn, A

171

CHORUS

boy's best friend is his Mo-ther._____ Then cher-ish her with care, And

smooth her sil-v'ry hair, When gone you will nev-er get an-

-o-ther._____ And where-ev-er we may turn, This

colla voce

rall.

les-son we shall learn, A boy's best friend is his Mo-ther._____

172

A Boy's Best Friend is His Mother

1. While plodding on our way, the toilsome road of life,
   How few the friends that daily there we meet!
   Not many will stand by in trouble and in strife,
   With counsel and affection ever sweet!
   But there is one whose smile, will ever on us beam,
   Whose love is dearer far than any other
   And wherever we may turn,
   This lesson we will learn,
   A boy's best friend is his Mother.

CHORUS: Then cherish her with care,
   And smooth her silv'ry hair,
   When gone you will never get another.
   And wherever we may turn,
   This lesson we shall learn,
   A boy's best friend is his Mother.

2. Tho' all the world may frown, and ev'ry friend depart,
   She never will forsake us in our need!
   Our refuge evermore is still within her heart,
   For us her loving sympathy will plead!
   Her pure and gentle smile, for ever cheers our way,
   'Tis sweeter and 'tis purer than all other.
   When she goes from earth away,
   We'll find out while we stray,
   A boy's best friend is his Mother.

CHORUS: Then cherish her with care, etc.

3. Her fond and gentle face not long may greet us here,
   Then cheer her with our kindness and our love!
   Remember at her knee in childhood bright and dear,
   We heard her voice, like angel's from above.
   Tho' after years may bring, their gladness or their woe,
   Her love is sweeter far than any other.
   And our longing heart will learn,
   Wherever we may turn,
   A boy's best friend is his Mother.

CHORUS: Then cherish her with care, etc.

Joseph P. Skelly, who composed this song in 1883, was an American plumber who wrote about four hundred songs. A victim of constant dissipation, he sold many of his ballads for practically nothing to buy liquor. Other songs he composed were the famous 'The Old Rustic Bridge by the Mill', 'The Picture That is Turned Towards the Wall', 'My Pretty Red Rose' and, with words by George Cooper, 'Strolling on Brooklyn Bridge'. Unsympathetic commentators have observed that the maudlin style of 'A Boy's Best Friend is His Mother' may have something to do with Skelly's drinking habits, but that does not explain the rather fetching melody. There is something intangibly American about it: it could never have been written in the Old World.

Maggie Murphy's Home

Written by EDWARD HARRIGAN

Composed by DAVE BRAHAM

1. Be - hind a gram - mar school - house In a dou - ble ten - e - ment, I live with my old mo - ther And

Fine

Maggie Murphy's Home

al - ways pay the rent;_____ A bed room

and a par - lor_____ Is all we call our

own, And__ you're wel - come ev - 'ry eve - -

- ning At Mag - gie Mur - phy's home._____

CHORUS

On Sun - day night, 'tis my de - light And plea - sure

175

don't_ you see, _____ Meet-ing all the girls and

all the boys, That work down town_ with me,_____

___ There's an or - gan in_ the par - - lor To

give the house_ a tone, And_ you're wel - come ev - 'ry

eve - ning At Mag -gie Mur - phy's home_____

D. %

Maggie Murphy's Home

1. Behind a grammar school-house
   In a double tenement,
   I live with my old mother
   And always pay the rent;
   A bedroom and a parlor
   Is all we call our own,
   And you're welcome ev'ry evening
   At Maggie Murphy's home.

CHORUS: On Sunday night, 'tis my delight
And pleasure don't you see,
Meeting all the girls and all the boys,
That work down town with me,
There's an organ in the parlor
To give the house a tone,
And you're welcome ev'ry evening
At Maggie Murphy's home.

2. Such dancing in the parlor,
   There's a waltz for you and me;
   Such mashing in the corner,
   And kisses too, maybe:
   We bless the leisure hours
   To working people known,
   And they're welcome ev'ry evening
   At Maggie Murphy's home.

CHORUS: On Sunday night, 'tis my delight, etc.

3. It's from the open window
   At the noontime of the day,
   You'll see the neighbours' children
   So happy at their play;
   There's Jimmy with his Nelly
   Together romp and roam,
   And they gather in the school-yard
   Near Maggie Murphy's home.

CHORUS: On Sunday night, 'tis my delight, etc.

4. I walk through Hogan's Alley
   At the closing of the day,
   To greet my dear old mother,
   You'll hear the neighbours say:
   'Oh, there goes little Maggie,
   I wish she were my own:
   Oh, may blessings ever linger
   O'er Maggie Murphy's home.'

CHORUS: On Sunday night, 'tis my delight, etc.

The names of Harrigan and Hart are synonymous with entertainment in New York in the 'seventies and 'eighties. Their famous shows evolved into a unique and hilarious theatrical phenomenon, a mélange of related sketches and burlesques, usually with an Irish theme, liberally decorated with songs and music, the progenitor of musical comedy. Edward Harrigan (1845–1911), ex-seaman, began by joining in a double act with Tony Hart (really Anthony Cannon, 1855–1891), singer, dancer, comedian and female impersonator—the best 'genteel wench' in the business. Gradually, they built up complete shows: their first great success was *The Mulligan Guard*, which boasted a catchy march song that Rudyard Kipling reported as a favourite with British troops in India and which formed the basis for many variations on the Mulligan theme in future shows. The composer for Harrigan and Hart was an Englishman, David Braham (1838–1905), who emigrated to America to become a musical director for New York theatres. There were many famous songs, and our example here was a particular favourite with Irish immigrants who, no doubt, tried it out to the accompaniment of that organ in the parlour. It is certainly a piece that responds to performance by many voices.

177

Boys & Girls

or, Songs of Childhood

Watching for Pa

Written and composed by HENRY CLAY WORK

1. Three lit - tle forms in the twi - light gray,

180

Watching for Pa

Scan - ning the shad - ows a - cross the way; Two pair of black eyes, and one of blue, Brim - ful of love, and of mis - chief too: Watch-ing for Pa! Watch-ing for Pa! Sit - ting by the win - dow, Watch - ing for Pa!

Watching for Pa

1. Three little forms in the twilight gray,
    Scanning the shadows across the way;
  Two pair of black eyes, and one of blue,—
    Brimful of love, and of mischief too:
        Watching for Pa!
        Watching for Pa!
        Sitting by the window,
        Watching for Pa!

CHORUS: Watching for Pa!
        Watching for Pa!
        Sitting by the window,
        Watching for Pa!

2. May, with her placid and thoughtful brow,
    Beaming with kindness and love just now;
  Willie, the youngest, so roguish and gay,
    Stealing sly kisses from sister May.
        Watching for Pa!
        Watching for Pa!
        Sitting by the window,
        Watching for Pa!

CHORUS: Watching for Pa! etc.

3. Nellie, with ringlets of sunny hue,
    Cosily nestled between the two,
  Pressing her cheek to the window pane,
    Wishing the absent one home again.
        Watching for Pa!
        Watching for Pa!
        Sitting by the window,
        Watching for Pa!

CHORUS: Watching for Pa! etc.

4. Now there are shouts from the window seat,
    There is a patter of childish feet;
  Gaily they rush through the lighted hall—
    'Coming at last,' is the joyful call.
        Welcoming Pa!
        Welcoming Pa!
        Standing on the doorstep,
        Welcoming Pa!

CHORUS: Welcoming Pa!
        Welcoming Pa!
        Standing on the doorstep,
        Welcoming Pa!

One of Henry Clay Work's lesser-known songs, this conveys the whole feeling of those tender pictures, reproduced in oleograph, of chubby Victorian children with their rosebud mouths, wide eyes and curly golden locks. It is a sunny prelude to the pathetic ballads that follow with their cast of young innocents doomed to premature decease. Some notes on the composer of this song are to be found on page 169. This example of his work has a striking harmonic similarity to his 'Ring the Bell, Watchman' (on page 222).

Shall I be an Angel, Daddy?

Written by CHARLES COLLINS
and FRED J. BARNES

Composed by CHARLES COLLINS
Arranged by JOHN FRANCIS

1. One day a fa-ther to his lit-tle son Told a sad stor-y, a

heart break-ing one, He took from an al-bum a pho-to, and

185

said; "This is your mo-ther, but long she's been dead;

You she has left me to cher-ish and love, She is an

an-gel, my child, up a-bove." The boy in an in-stant drew

close to his side, And these are the words that he soft-ly re-plied:

CHORUS

"Shall I be an an-gel, dad-dy?_____ An an-gel in the

Shall I be an Angel, Daddy?

sky?_____ Will I wear the gold - en wings, And rest in

peace on high?_____ Shall I live for ev - er and ev - er

With the an - gels fair?_____ If I go to hea - ven, oh!

tell me, dad - dy, Will I see mo - ther there?"_____

Shall I be an Angel, Daddy?

One day a father to his little son
    Told a sad story, a heart-breaking one,
He took from an album a photo, and said,
    'This is your mother, but long she's been dead;
You she has left me to cherish and love,
    She is an angel, my child, up above.'
The boy in an instant drew close to his side,
    And these are the words that he softly replied:

CHORUS: 'Shall I be an angel, daddy?
    An angel in the sky?
    Will I wear the golden wings,
    And rest in peace on high?
    Shall I live for ever and ever
    With the angels fair?
    If I go to heaven, oh! tell me, daddy,
    Will I see mother there?'

The previous song belonged to the impeccable drawing-room school; this comes from the music-hall of 1897. The sentiments are very similar, and the song boasts a very fetching chorus. The setting is quite delightful; it is the perfect ideal of what adults felt a child's song should be. Notice, particularly, the piano being an angel in the sky at bars seven and eight of the chorus.

Charles Collins had a hand in many popular songs. He joined with Fred W. Leigh to produce the famous 'Don't Dilly Dally by the Way' and a number of others. Fred J. Barnes was a music-hall singer who, like many stars of the turn of the century, glittered for a while before burning out.

Saved by a Child

Written by 'NEMO'

Composed by M. PICCOLOMINI

Andante cantabile

1. 'Twas a gold - en, ra - diant Sab-bath morn; I stood by the Min - ster' gate My heart was wea - ry, crush'd and torn By the ruth - less hand of Fate. I gaz'd, in a mood of un - be

Con moto

189

lief,   On the crowd   that throng'd   the aisle;   And

yet,   with a long-ing   for re - lief,   I   en - ter'd the sa - cred

Grandioso

pile: Su - blime   was   the or-gan's thrill - ing peal!   Tri-

- um - phant   the voi   -   ces   soar'd!

agitato

Oh!   to my heart could they but   steal,   And

bound me to Earth, and earth - ly things, E'en in the

House of the King of Kings!

2. But lo! at the hour of ev - en-tide, I

stood in a si - lent room; Where a child and mo-ther, side by

side, Knelt in the twi - light gloom, And the

Saved by a Child

193

Saved by a Child

Change in - to flow'rs with-in his hands, And, by

him, are borne a - way; A - -

- way! A - way! on his migh - - ty wings, To the

throne of the King of Kings!

Saved by a Child

1. 'Twas a golden, radiant Sabbath morn;
    I stood by the Minster gate.
   My heart was weary, crush'd and torn
    By the ruthless hand of Fate.
   I gaz'd, in a mood of unbelief,
    On the crowd that throng'd the aisle;
   And yet, with a longing for relief,
    I enter'd the sacred pile:
   Sublime was the organ's thrilling peal!
    Triumphant the voices soar'd!
   Oh! to my heart could they but steal,
    And strike one responsive chord!
   I kneel, and clasp my fev'rish hands;
    But, alas! I cannot pray!
   For there, by my side, a shadow stands;
    And my passions, in fierce conflict,
   Have bound me to Earth, and earthly things,
    E'en in the House of the King of Kings!

2. But lo! at the hour of even-tide,
    I stood in a silent room;
   Where a child and mother, side by side,
    Knelt in the twilight gloom,
   And the child, in falt'ring accents told
    To the Heav'ns his touching plea;
   And a wave of comfort o'er me roll'd,
    Like the tide of some deep sea!
   O list to the soft silv'ry voice,
    Lisping that pray'r of pray'rs!
   Rejoice, my chasten'd heart, rejoice!
    And spurn thine earthly cares:
   For, at the gates of Heav'n an angel stands,
    And the pray'rs that children pray
   Change into flow'rs within his hands,
    And, by him, are borne away;
   Away! Away! on his mighty wings,
    To the throne of the King of Kings!

Théodore Auguste Marie Joseph Piccolomini (1835–1902), born in Dublin, wrote under the name of Henry Pontet a great many popular ballads, and under his own name sacred songs, selling them very often for trifling sums. One of the best known, 'Ora Pro Nobis', went for a five-pound note. He was so prolific a composer and delivered to his publisher so many ballads that were never performed, that at his death the office safe was crammed with Piccolomini's manuscripts—and I.O.Us. He should not be confused with the Italian singer, Maria Piccolomini.

The Burial of the Linnet

Written by J. H. EWING   Composed by SIR ALFRED SCOTT-GATTY

1. Found in the gar - den,— dead in his beau - ty.

Ah! that a lin - net should die in the Spring!

Bu - ry him, com - rades, in pi - ti - ful du - ty,

Muf - fle the din - ner bell,— so - lemn - ly ring.

The Burial of the Linnet

1. Found in the garden,— dead in his beauty.
    Ah! that a linnet should die in the Spring!
   Bury him, comrades, in pitiful duty,
    Muffle the dinner bell, solemnly ring.

2. Bury him kindly—up in the corner;
    Bird, beast, and gold-fish are sepulchred there.
   Bid the black kitten march as chief mourner,
    Waving her tail like a plume in the air.

3. Bury him nobly—next to the donkey;
    Fetch the old banner, and wave it about;
   Bury him deeply—think of the monkey:
    Shallow his grave, and the dogs got him out.

4. Bury him softly—white wool around him
    Kiss his poor feathers—the first kiss and last;
   Tell his poor widow kind friends have found him:
    Plant his poor grave with whatever grows fast.

5. Farewell, sweet singer! dead in thy beauty,
    Silent through summer, though other birds sing,
   Bury him, comrades, in pitiful duty,
    Muffle the dinner bell, mournfully ring.

The children for whom this little song was written were early introduced to the facts of death. Any glance into juvenile literature of the mid-century will reveal a constant preoccupation with the decease of other little folk, close relatives, pets and dolls. For those nurtured on Grimm, a touch of the gruesome would not have come as a surprise. Nevertheless, one cannot but raise an eyebrow at the curious humour of the third stanza.

Sir Alfred Scott-Gatty (1847–1918) and Juliana Horatia Orr Ewing (1841–1885) were brother and sister, children of the Vicar of Ecclesfield in Yorkshire, Rev. Alfred Scott Gatty, himself a prolific writer and author of a standard work on bells. Little Juliana was a born story-teller and actress (the latter tendency her mother had firmly to discourage) and wrote nursery plays for the family, performed with her brother Alfred as musical conductor. When she was twenty Juliana published three stories, and as her mother, Margaret Gatty, was editor of *Aunt Judy's Magazine*, she became a regular contributor and developed into one of the most famous of Victorian children's writers. Her domestic moral tales are now too religious for modern tastes, but her fairy stories remain enchanting. *The Brownies* and *A Flat Iron for a Farthing* are among her best-known books. She married Major Alexander Ewing of the Army Pay Corps, a cultivated man who wrote hymns, including 'Jerusalem the Golden'. When Alfred grew up he continued to compose, producing songs, operettas and musical plays for children. His chief calling, however, was heraldry and genealogy. He hyphenated his name and rose to the lofty post of Garter King-of-Arms in 1904.

Won't You Buy My Pretty Flowers?

Written by A. W. FRENCH

Composed by G. W. PERSLEY

1. Un-der neath the gas-light's glit-ter, Stands a lit-tle fra-gile girl, Heed-less of the night winds bit-ter, As they round a-bout her whirl, While the hun-dreds pass un-heed-ing, In the

Won't You Buy My Pretty Flowers?

1. Underneath the gaslight's glitter,
    Stands a little fragile girl,
  Heedless of the night winds bitter,
    As they round about her whirl,
  While the hundreds pass unheeding,
    In the ev'ning's waning hours,
  Still she cries with tearful pleading,
    'Won't you buy my pretty flowers?'

CHORUS: There are many, sad and weary,
      In this pleasant world of ours,
      Crying ev'ry night so dreary,
      'Won't you buy my pretty flowers?'

2. Ever coming, ever going,
    Men and women hurry by,
  Heedless of the teardrops gleaming
    In her sad and wistful eye.
  How her little heart is sighing
    In the cold and dreary hours;
  Only listen to her crying,
    'Won't you buy my pretty flowers?

CHORUS: There are many, sad and weary,
      etc.

3. Not a loving word to cheer her
    From the passers by is heard,
  Not a friend to linger near her,
    With her heart by pity stirred;
  Homeward goes the tide of fashion,
    Seeking pleasure's pleasant bowers;
  None to hear with sad compassion,
    'Won't you buy my pretty flowers?'

CHORUS: There are many, sad and weary,
      etc.

The little heroine of this song is descended directly from Dickens's Little Nell, and no doubt she stimulated kindly ladies to even greater efforts in their charitable work. An American ballad in the waltz time necessary for true pathos, this was taken to England by the Minstrels and had an immense vogue. The second bar of the song will strike musicians as a clear case of 'square-piano' harmony. Probably a 6/4 chord on G would sound better on one of today's instruments.

Tatters

Written and composed by GERALD LANE

1. Tat-ters, with his lit-tle broom,
2. One day came a lit-tle maid

Stands a-mid the crowd, In the sun-shine, in the gloom,
Sel-ling ro-ses there, So de-mure-ly coy and staid,

Where the strife is loud. Lords and la-dies, fine and fair,
So di-vine-ly fair. Tat-ters thought her face more sweet

Tatters

Pass him as he lin - gers there; Prince and pea - sant swell the throng,
Than the ros - es at her feet, Look'd in - to her eyes of gray,

Hour by hour that crowds a - long.
Till he look'd his heart a - way.

REFRAIN

Ah! Rags and Tat - ters,__
Ah! Rags and Tat - ters,__

'Neath the ci - ty sky,__ For - tune lit - tle mat - ters__ When
'Neath the ci - ty sky,__ For - tune lit - tle mat - ters__ When

Hope beats high,__ For - tune lit - tle mat - ters When Hope beats
Love is nigh,__ For - tune lit - tle mat - ters When Love is

high! __
nigh! __

D. % p Più lento

3. Years have pass'd a - way since then,

Tat - ters, old and gray,___ Now has rich - es, pow'r and place,

So the peo - ple say,___ But his lit - tle love of yore,

marcato il canto

rall. e dim.

Smiles up - on him nev - er - more, Where the white moon - dais - ies wave,

rall. e dim.

Tatters

Tat ters kneels be - side her grave. Ah! lone - ly Tat - ters,

Sad - ly now you sigh,___ "For - tune lit - tle mat - ters___ If

Love goes by,___ For - tune lit - tle mat - ters If

Love, If Love goes by!"___

Tatters

1. Tatters, with his little broom,
    Stands amid the crowd,
In the sunshine, in the gloom,
    Where the strife is loud.
Lords and ladies, fine and fair,
    Pass him as he lingers there;
Prince and peasant swell the throng,
    Hour by hour that crowds along.

REFRAIN: Ah! Rags and Tatters,
    'Neath the city sky,
    Fortune little matters
    When Hope beats high,
    Fortune little matters
    When Hope beats high!

2. One day came a little maid
    Selling roses there,
So demurely coy and staid,
    So divinely fair.
Tatters thought her face more sweet
    Than the roses at her feet;
Look'd into her eyes of gray,
    Till he look'd his heart away.

REFRAIN: Ah! Rags and Tatters,
    'Neath the city sky,
    Fortune little matters
    When Love is nigh,
    Fortune little matters
    When Love is nigh!

3. Years have pass'd away since then,
    Tatters, old and gray,
Now has riches, pow'r and place,
    So the people say,
But his little love of yore,
    Smiles upon him nevermore,
Where the white moon-daisies wave,
    Tatters kneels beside her grave.

REFRAIN: Ah! lonely Tatters,
    Sadly now you sigh,
    'Fortune little matters
    If Love goes by,
    Fortune little matters
    If Love goes by!'

Tatters is a British waif, and his ballad, according to Maurice Willson Disher in *Victorian Song*, was sung by 'horrible little boys everywhere'. In fact, this is a very accomplished piece of writing for the voice in a style well before its time. The more interesting piano interpolations and the abrupt minor/major change for the chorus, also, make the setting very forward-looking.

Auntie

Written by FRED E. WEATHERLY   Composed by A. H. BEHREND

1. You're my lit - tle true lov - er, You're my lit - tle boy blue,___ But

I'm your old Aunt - ie, dar - ling, And I can - not mar - ry you. 'Tis

Auntie

2. No one has mar-ried me, dar - ling, How can I tell you why? 'Tis such an old__ old sto - ry, 'Tis such a while gone by. No one has mar-ried me, dar - ling, No one will mar-ry me now, For who would mar - ry an old maid With wrin - kles on her brow? But you're my lit - tle true

rall.

a tempo

-bout me, Was I cross and sour and grey, Tell her the clouds will

ga-ther,— One can-not al-ways be gay.— Tell her I loved you, dar-ling,

Tell her for you I pray,— Old maids have hearts, my dar-ling, What-

-ev-er the world may say.

Auntie

1. You're my little true lover,
     You're my little boy blue,
   But I'm your old Auntie, darling,
     And I cannot marry you.
   'Tis grand to be six years old, dear,
     With pence in a money box,
   To ride on a wooden horse, dear,
     And leave off baby socks,
   'Tis grand to be going to school, dear,
     'Tis fine to be dress'd in blue,
   But I'm your old Auntie, darling,
     And I cannot marry you.

2. No one has married me, darling,
     How can I tell you why?
   'Tis such an old old story,
     'Tis such a while gone by.
   No one has married me, darling,
     No one will marry me now,
   For who would marry an old maid
     With wrinkles on her brow?
   But you're my little true lover,
     You're my little boy blue,
   And I love to think that the whole world
     Is happy and bright like you.

3. One will marry you, darling,
     When you're a man one day,
   Who'll love and cherish you, darling,
     When Auntie is gone away,
   And if she should ask about me,
     Was I cross and sour and grey,
   Tell her the clouds will gather,
     One cannot always be gay.
   Tell her I loved you, darling,
     Tell her for you I pray,
   Old maids have hearts, my darling,
     Whatever the world may say.

Weatherly recounts in his autobiography how Behrend tried several times to set the lyric of 'Auntie'. James Molloy asked for the chance of providing the music, but Behrend requested another week's grace and completed the song. It was rendered exquisitely by Madame Patey at the Crystal Palace and the audience loved it. The critics were rather less enthusiastic and 'a daily paper of considerable importance' described it 'somewhat as follows': 'A song of a little boy in love with his aunt; a disgraceful song; a disgrace to the author, to the composer, to the singer and to the publisher.' Weatherly took great offence and was all for going to law about it, but was dissuaded by his solicitor. His rancour must have been mollified by the great success of the ballad. Behrend composed another song capitalising on 'Auntie's' popularity. It was called 'Daddy' and sold over a million copies in sheet music.

    Arthur Henry Behrend (1853–1935) was born in Danzig of a noble Swedish family, the grandson, on his mother's side, of M. W. Balfe, from whom, no doubt, he inherited his melodic gifts. Young Behrend came to England as a boy and received a good public-school education at Haileybury, becoming a member of the First XI. After a year in business, he studied music under Reinecke and Richter. As a composer he had a published output of more than two hundred songs, and he also wrote cantatas and (unpublished) operas.

Sacred & Sentimental

or, Songs of Inspiration

The Last Rose of Summer

Written by THOMAS MOORE, music traditional

Andante moderato

1. 'Tis the last rose of _____ sum-mer Left_____ bloom - ing _____ a - lone, All her love - ly com - -pan-ions Are____ fad___ ed and___ gone! No____

The Last Rose of Summer

The Last Rose of Summer

1. 'Tis the last rose of summer
   Left blooming alone,
   All her lovely companions
   Are faded and gone!
   No flower of her kindred,
   No rosebud is nigh
   To reflect back her blushes,
   Or give sigh for sigh.

2. I'll not leave thee, thou lone one,
   To pine on the stem;
   Since the lovely are sleeping,
   Go, sleep thou with them:
   Thus kindly I scatter
   Thy leaves o'er the bed
   Where thy mates of the garden
   Lie scentless and dead.

3. So soon may I follow,
   When friendships decay,
   And from love's shining circle,
   The gems drop away,
   When true hearts lie wither'd,
   And fond ones are flown,
   Oh! who would inhabit
   This bleak world alone.

The melody of 'The Last Rose of Summer' has a complicated history. In its earliest known form it was a street ballad of about 1660, purveyed by travelling harpers around Ireland. The tune was adopted by an itinerant bard, by profession a weaver, named Barrett, who used it in 'Castle Hyde', an extravagant musical jibe at the Hyde family who had slighted him. Once again it was borrowed in the eighteenth century by Richard Alfred Milliken who presented it to the world as 'The Groves of Blarney', and Thomas Moore took it in this garb as an ancient song. It is also said to have appeared under the guise of 'The Young Man's Dream' in a couple of collections of songs in the 1790s. Thomas Moore worked over it yet again (indeed, it has been ascribed totally to him), providing new and more euphonious words, and published it in 1813 as one of his *Irish Melodies*.

Moore, who had a small but very sweet voice, sang these pieces to his own accompaniment, often moving his auditors, as well as himself, to tears. 'The Last Rose' was a great favourite with the early nineteenth-century soprano, Catherine Hayes. After one performance of it at the Limerick Theatre Royal, as the applause died down a boy in the gallery shouted, 'Once again, Catherine darlin'! Sure, your mother was a nightingale!'

It received a new lease of life in mid-century when it was introduced into *Martha* by Count Frederick von Flotow, an opera founded upon a ballet, which was first produced in Vienna in 1847, reaching London ten years later. It received phenomenal public acclaim but a patchy critical reception. Berlioz, who detested Flotow, remarked, 'the beauty of the Irish melody served to disinfect the rottenness of the *Martha* music'. But Berlioz had special cause to appreciate the song. Under the influence of the Irish Shakespearean actress, Harriet Smithson, whom he later married, he set in 1830 a selection of Moore's pieces as *Neuf Mélodies Irlandaises*. So well-received were they that the French word for 'song', 'chanson', was overtaken by 'mélodie'.

The *Irish Melodies* formed the foundation stone of Victorian balladry with their melting melodies married to sentiments of unimpeachable respectability. Many of them are still immensely popular: 'The Last Rose of Summer', 'Oft in the Stilly Night', 'The

Minstrel Boy', 'The Harp That Once through Tara's Hall's', 'Dear Harp of My Country', 'The Meeting of the Waters' and 'Believe Me If All Those Endearing Young Charms'. Over a million and a half copies of 'The Last Rose of Summer' were sold in America alone. Most people accepted Moore's pieces as genuine Hibernian airs, but by the end of the century scholars were waxing extremely critical of his handling of the originals, not all of which were Irish to begin with. Moore had been doing, of course, what many in his period had tried, an 'improvement' of rude country ballads to make them acceptable in the drawing-room.

Thoms Moore (1779–1852), the Irish poet, began to publish his first verses at the age of fourteen. Like so many of his compatriots, he found Dublin too small for him and he emigrated to London, where his musical gifts brought him social success. Some amorous poetry of his, a little less discreet than was *de rigeur*, caused a mild public flutter, but his charm kept him in genteel favour. He toured America and Canada, and returned home to write 'The Canadian Boat Song'. From 1807 to 1834 he brought out his *Irish Melodies* at a remuneration of £100 per song, the musical arrangements being by Sir John Stevenson. He wrote some heavy satires, married an actress, moved in the most brilliant society and became a friend of Lord Byron. Moore incurred the heavy displeasure of posterity when, for the best of moral reasons, he burned Byron's memoirs after his death.

O for the Wings of a Dove!

Written by WILLIAM BARTHOLOMEW

Composed by FELIX MENDELSSOHN BARTHOLDY

O__ for the wings, for the wings of a dove! Far a-way, far a-

-way would I rove! O__ for the wings, for the wings__ of a dove!

far a-way, far a-way, far a-way, far a-

O for the Wings of a Dove!

way would I rove, In the wil - der-ness build me a nest,____ And re-

-main__ there for ev - er at rest,____ In the wil - der-ness build me

build me a nest__ And re - main there for ev - er at rest,

In____ the wil - der-ness build me a nest,__ And re - main there for

219

O for the Wings of a Dove!

O for the wings, for the wings of a dove!
   Far away, far away would I rove!
In the wilderness build me a nest,
   And remain there for ever at rest.

It is possible that inspiration for this song came from 'The Wings of the Dove', a piece by that prolific poetess Dorothea Felicia Hemans, who wrote 'Casabianca' ('The boy stood on the burning deck . . .'). The first stanza of Mrs Hemans's poem runs:

Oh, for thy wings, thou dove!
   Now sailing by with sunshine on thy breast;
   That, borne like thee above,
I too might flee away, and be at rest!

The version of the song printed here is that usually sung by boy sopranos; there is a longer setting, more suitable for performance with full chorus. It is guaranteed to show off the voice to advantage, and the beautiful soaring melody really does take wing.

'O for the Wings of a Dove!' is part of Mendelssohn's anthem with organ accompaniment *Hear My Prayer*. This was written in January 1844 for William Bartholomew (1793–1867), whom Grove calls Mendelssohn's 'careful and laborious translator of his works into English'. Besides an adapter of Mendelssohn's work, Bartholomew was a highly-accomplished violinist, librettist and artist, with a wife famous in her own right as an organist and composer of cantata and part songs.

Felix Mendelssohn Bartholdy (1809–1847) formed with Chopin and Schumann the great romantic trio. They were all born within a year of each other. Mendelssohn's standing a hundred years ago was on the pinnacle of musical celebrity. With Gounod and Spohr he had enjoyed the patronage of Queen Victoria and the Prince Consort, and pre-eminently among these three composers he introduced a style that became one of the cornerstones of 'English' compositional style, hitherto almost entirely dominated by Handel. His reputation became a little fly-blown by the opening of this century; many critics found him charming, beautiful, musicianly, but also, alas, facile, harmless, and occasionally cheap. Perhaps he had produced too much and had too great an early success. He was a boy prodigy who had completed fifteen symphonies by his fifteenth birthday. It is pleasant to record that today his true value is being realised.

Ring the Bell, Watchman

Written and composed by HENRY CLAY WORK

1. High in the bel - fry the old sex - ton stands,

Grasp - ing the rope with his thin bo - ny hands,

Fix'd is his gaze as by some mag - ic spell,

Ring the Bell, Watchman

Till he hears the dis-tant mur-mur, Ring, ring the bell!

CHORUS

Ring the bell, Watch-man, ring, ring, ring; Yes, yes, the good news is

now on the wing; Yes, yes, they come and with tid-ings to tell,

Glo-ri-ous and bless-ed tid-ings, Ring, ring the bell.

Ring the Bell, Watchman

1. High in the belfry the old sexton stands,
    Grasping the rope with his thin bony hands,
  Fix'd is his gaze as by some magic spell,
    Till he hears the distant murmur, Ring, ring the bell!

CHORUS: Ring the bell, Watchman, ring, ring, ring;
        Yes, yes, the good news is now on the wing;
        Yes, yes, they come and with tidings to tell,
        Glorious and blessed tidings,
        Ring, ring the bell.

2. Baring his long silver locks to the breeze,
    First for a moment he drops on his knees,
  Then with a vigour that few could excel
    Answers he the welcome bidding, Ring, ring the bell!

CHORUS: Ring the bell, Watchman, etc.

3. Hear from the hill top the first signal gun
    Thunders the word that some great deed is done;
  Hear thro' the valley the long echoes swell,
    Ever and anon repeating, Ring, ring the bell!

CHORUS: Ring the bell, Watchman, etc.

4. Bonfires are blazing and rockets ascend,
    No meagre triumph such tokens portend,
  Shout, shout, my brothers, for all, all is well,
    'Tis the universal chorus, Ring, ring the bell!

CHORUS: Ring the bell, Watchman, etc.

Here is Work at his most tuneful; the swinging march is reminiscent of several Civil War songs and even has a touch of 'Davy Crockett', clearly by the same composer as 'Marching through Georgia'. It also shows Work at his most morally invigorating; the good news now on the wing is unspecified, but there is little doubt that evangelical protestantism has triumphed again. Australian readers will recognise here the melody of their folk song, 'Click Go the Shears'.

There are some notes on Henry Clay Work on page 169.

224

Waste Not, Want Not

(*You Never Miss the Water Till the Wells Runs Dry*)

Composed by ROLLIN HOWARD

1. When a child I liv'd at Lin-coln, with my par-ents at the farm, The les-sons that my mo-ther taught, to me were quite a charm, She would oft-en take me on her knee when tir'd of child-ish play, And

225

as she press'd me to her breast, I've heard my mo - ther say -

CHORUS
f

Waste not, want not, is a max - im I would teach,

Let your watch - word be des - patch, and prac - tise what you preach,

Do not let your chan - ces, like sun - beams pass you by, For you

nev – er miss the wat – er till the well runs___ dry.

Waste Not, Want Not

1. When a child I liv'd at Lincoln, with my parents at the farm,
   The lessons that my mother taught, to me were quite a charm,
   She would often take me on her knee when tir'd of childish play,
   And as she press'd me to her breast, I heard my mother say—

CHORUS: Waste not, want not, is a maxim I would teach,
      Let your watchword be despatch and practise what you preach,
      Do not let your chances, like sunbeams pass you by,
      For you never miss the water till the well runs dry.

2. As years roll'd on I grew to be a mischief making boy,
   Destruction seem'd my only sport, it was my only joy,
   And well do I remember, when oft times well chastis'd,
   How father sat beside me then, and thus has me advis'd—

CHORUS: Waste not, want not, etc.

3. When I arriv'd at manhood, I embark'd in public life,
   And found it was a rugged road, bestrewn with care and strife;
   I speculated foolishly, my losses were severe,
   But still a tiny little voice kept whisp'ring in my ear—

CHORUS: Waste not, want not, etc.

4. Then I studied strict economy, and found to my surprise,
   My funds instead of sinking, very quickly then did rise,
   I grasp'd each chance and always struck the iron while 'twas hot,
   I seiz'd my opportunities and never once forgot—

CHORUS: Waste not, want not, etc.

5. I'm married now and happy, I've a careful little wife,
   We live in peace and harmony, devoid of care and strife,
   For Fortune smiles upon us, we have little children three,
   The lesson that I teach them, as they prattle 'round my knee—

CHORUS: Waste not, want not, etc.

This cheerful American embodiment of the basic teachings of the Protestant ethic with its rather saucy tune is one of the many 'adage' songs that were popular from 1870 onwards. The authorship is credited to Rollin or Roland Howard, but it has also been claimed by Harry Linn. It was a particular favourite of Minstrel shows. Of the inevitable parodies, there is one entitled 'You Never Miss the Lager Till the Keg Runs Dry'.

Goodbye!

Written by G. J. Whyte-Melville   Composed by Sir F. Paolo Tosti

Goodbye!

swal-lows are mak-ing them rea-dy to fly, Wheel-ing out on a

rit. **pp** *lentamente*

win-dy— sky— Good-bye, Sum-mer! Good-bye, Good-

col canto *molto legato* **pp**

cresc.

- bye, Good-bye, sum-mer! Good-bye, Good — bye!

rit.

cresc. *col canto* **pp**

p

molto rall.

2. Hush! A voice from the far - a - way! "Lis-ten and

poco più

229

learn", it seems to say, "All the to-mor-rows shall be as to-day." "All the to-mor-rows shall be as to-day." The cord is frayed — the cruse is dry, The link must break, and the lamp must die. Good-bye, to Hope! Good-bye, Good-bye, Good-bye, to Hope! Good-bye, Good-bye!

Goodbye!

3. What are we wait - ing for? Oh! my heart!

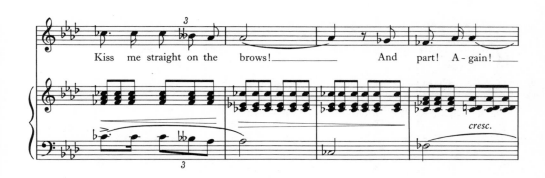

Kiss me straight on the brows!_____ And part! A - gain!_____

_____ A - gain!_____ my heart!_____ my heart! What are we wait - ing

for, you and I? A plead - ing look

Goodbye!

1. Falling leaf, and fading tree,
   Lines of white on a sullen sea,
   Shadows rising on you and me;
   Shadows rising on you and me;
   The swallows are making them ready to fly,
   Wheeling out on a windy sky.
   Goodbye, Summer! Goodbye, Goodbye,
   Goodbye, Summer! Goodbye, Goodbye!

2. Hush! A voice from the faraway!
   'Listen and learn,' it seems to say,
   'All the tomorrows shall be as today.'
   'All the tomorrows shall be as today.'
   The cord is frayed—the cruse is dry,
   The link must break, and the lamp must die.
   Goodbye, to Hope! Goodbye, Goodbye,
   Goodbye, to Hope! Goodbye, Goodbye!

3. What are we waiting for? Oh! my heart!
   Kiss me straight on the brows! And part!
   Again! Again! my heart! my heart!
   What are we waiting for, you and I?
   A pleading look—a stifled cry.
   Goodbye, for ever! Goodbye, for ever!
   Goodbye, Goodbye, Goodbye!

Here is a prime example of the art ballad, a form heard in the drawing-room rather than the parlour. The melody, obviously harmonically conceived, justifies its reputation. A sensitive rendering can be very appealing, and perhaps cover up the composer's slight over-enthusiasm for chromaticism for its own sake.

George John Whyte-Melville (1821–1878) was an ex-Guardsman who had served with the Turks in the Crimea and made a name as a novelist specialising in fox-hunting situations. He died after an accident in the hunting field, but his literary work was not exclusively sporting; he wrote a number of songs including 'Drink Puppy, Drink' and the still popular 'Wrap Me Up in My Tarpaulin Jacket'.

Sir Francesco Paolo Tosti (1846–1916) was born in Ortona, and made his name as a songwriter in Italy, receiving royal approbation from the Queen of that country. She heard him sing and immediately appointed him her singing teacher. He first visited London in 1875 and became popular in the best circles. Five years later he settled in England, became teacher of singing to the Royal Family, and sang duets with Queen Victoria and with Queen Alexandra. Tosti was an elegant composer, his Italian melodic flow controlled by a delicacy and simplicity that won him a great following in the most polite of salons.

The Lost Chord

Written by ADELAIDE A. PROCTER

Composed by SIR ARTHUR SULLIVAN

1. Seat-ed one day at the or-gan, I was wea-ry and ill at ease, And my fin-gers wan-der'd i-dly O-ver the noi-sy keys; I

The Lost Chord

The Lost Chord

1. Seated one day at the organ,
      I was weary and ill at ease,
   And my fingers wander'd idly
      Over the noisy keys;
   I know not what I was playing,
      Or what I was dreaming then,
   But I struck one chord of music,
      Like the sound of a great Amen,
      Like the sound of a great Amen.

2. It flooded the crimson twilight,
      Like the close of an Angel's Psalm,
   And it lay on my fever'd spirit,
      With a touch of infinite calm,
   It quieted pain and sorrow,
      Like love overcoming strife,
   It seem'd the harmonious echo
      From our discordant life,
   It link'd all perplexed meanings,
      Into one perfect peace,
   And trembled away into silence,
      As if it were loth to cease;
   I have sought, but I seek it vainly,
      That one lost chord divine,
   Which came from the soul of the organ,
      And enter'd into mine.

3. It may be that Death's bright Angel,
      Will speak in that chord again;
   It may be that only in Heav'n,
      I shall hear that grand Amen.
   (*Repeat these four lines*)

Fred, Arthur Sullivan's actor brother, had appeared in operettas, including *Trial by Jury*, and was about to take an important role in *The Sorcerer* when he fell ill. Three weeks later he died, on January 18th, 1877. Sullivan watched by his bedside night and day during those dreadful weeks. One night, towards the end, Sullivan chanced on the verses by Adelaide Procter that he had tried to set to music five years previously. He looked over them again and, in doing so, conceived their 'musical equivalent'. He worked through the night to complete the setting. Shortly afterwards Madame Antoinette Sterling asked him to set the very same words. 'I *have* set them,' replied Sullivan. Sterling sang at the first performance, with the composer at the piano and Sydney Naylor at the organ. Success was immediate and stupendous. 'I have composed much music since then,' remarked Sullivan later, 'but have never written a second "Lost Chord".' Indeed not. Many years after, Dame Clara Butt expressed what many have thought: 'What we need now is more songs like "The Lost Chord". There is something of the grandeur of Beethoven in it.'

There is certainly something of the dim religious light in it: Sullivan nurtured an ambition to be a church composer, and he wrote over fifty hymns, including 'Onward Christian Soldiers'. Despite some unfortunate lapses in word-setting, musically 'The Lost Chord' is superior to much of Sullivan's church music. To bring out its qualities to the full it should be sung to harmonium and piano accompaniment.

The eminent authority on popular song, Sigmund Spaeth, has confirmed its standing: 'Anyone doubting its place in a history of popular music should have heard it sung by the Flat Foot Four of Oklahoma City's police force in winning a barber-shop quartet contest at the New York World's Fair of 1940.'

Sir Arthur Sullivan (1842–1900) is now, of course, chiefly celebrated for his operettas, but he himself was half-ashamed of them. Well-meaning friends encouraged him to produce more respectable work. He produced oratorios, cantatas and a grand opera, *Ivanhoe*, but they are now almost totally forgotten. He had a great vogue, too, as a composer of ballads which exhibit the same gift for melody that made his operettas so popular.

Adelaide Anne Procter (1825–1864) was a noted English poetess, daughter of Bryan Waller Procter, a poet who called himself 'Barry Cornwall'. She wrote somewhat sad though inspiring pieces, and she perished from consumption. Curiously enough for a parlour bard, her main popularity came after her death, and she still had a great following in the early years of this century.

The Gypsy's Warning

Composed by HENRY A. GOARD

1. Do not trust him, gen-tle la - dy, Though his voice be low and sweet, Heed not him who kneels be - fore thee, Gen - tly plead - ing at thy feet. Now thy life is in — its

241

morn - ing, Cloud not this thy hap - py lot,

a tempo

Lis - ten to the gip - sy's warn - ing, Gen - tle la - dy, trust him

a tempo   *rit.*

not, Lis - ten to the gip - sy's warn - ing, Gen - tle

a tempo

la - dy, trust him not.

D.S.

The Gipsy's Warning

1. Do not trust him, gentle lady,
    Though his voice be low and sweet,
  Heed not him who kneels before thee,
    Gently pleading at thy feet.
  Now thy life is in its morning,
    Cloud not this thy happy lot,
  Listen to the gipsy's warning,
    Gentle lady, trust him not,
  Listen to the gipsy's warning,
    Gentle lady, trust him not.

2. Do not turn so coldly from me,
    I would only guard thy youth
  From his stern and with'ring power,
    I would only tell thee truth;
  I would shield thee from all danger,
    Save thee from the tempter's snare,
  Lady, shun that dark-ey'd stranger,
    I have warn'd thee, now beware,
  Lady, shun that dark-ey'd stranger,
    I have warn'd thee, now beware.

3. Lady, once there liv'd a maiden,
    Pure and bright, and like thee, fair,
  But he wooed, and wooed, and won her,
    Fill'd her gentle heart with care;
  Then he heeded not her weeping,
    Nor car'd he her life to save;
  Soon she perish'd, now she's sleeping
    In the cold and silent grave.
  Soon she perish'd, now she's sleeping
    In the cold and silent grave.

4. Keep thy gold, I do not wish it!
    Lady, I have pray'd for this,
  For the hour when I might foil him,
    Rob him of expected bliss;
  Gentle lady, do not wonder
    At my words so cold and wild,
  Lady, in that green grave, yonder,
    Lies the gipsy's only child,
  Lady, in that green grave, yonder,
    Lies the gipsy's only child.

This ballad, of which almost everyone knows the first line, was a Minstrel song, but the present editor has not been able to discover more about it and would welcome additional information.

Rum & True Religion

or, Songs of the Blue Ribbon

Come Home, Father

Written and composed by HENRY CLAY WORK

Come Home, Father

you would come home As soon as your day's work was done;____ Our fire has gone out — our house is all dark — And mo-ther's been watching since tea,____ With poor bro-ther Ben-ny so sick in her arms, And no one to help her but me.____ Come home, come home, come home,____ Please, fa-ther, dear fa-ther, come home. ____

Come Home, Father

Who could re-sist this most plain-tive of pray'rs? Please,

who could re-sist this most plain-tive of pray'rs? Please,

who could re-sist this most plain-tive of pray'rs? Please,

Who could re-sist this most plain-tive of pray'rs? Please,

fa-ther, dear fa-ther, come home.

fa-ther, dear fa-ther, come home.

fa-ther, dear fa-ther, come home.

fa-ther, dear fa-ther, come home.

D.S.

Come Home, Father

1. Father, dear father, come home with me now!
    The clock in the steeple strikes one;
   You promis'd, dear father, that you would come home
    As soon as your day's work was done;
   Our fire has gone out—our house is all dark—
    And mother's been watching since tea,
   With poor brother Benny so sick in her arms,
    And no one to help her but me.
   Come home, come home, come home,
    Please, father, dear father, come home.

CHORUS: Hear the sweet voice of the child,
        Which the night-winds repeat as they roam!
        Oh! who could resist this most plaintive of pray'rs?
        Please, father, dear father, come home.

2. Father, dear father, come home with me now!
    The clock in the steeple strikes two;
   The night has grown colder and Benny is worse—
    But he has been calling for you.
   Indeed he is worse—Ma says he will die,
    Perhaps before morning shall dawn;
   And this is the message she sent me to bring:
    'Come quickly, or he will be gone.'
   Come home, come home, come home,
    Please, father, dear father, come home.

CHORUS: Hear the sweet voice of the child, etc.

3. Father, dear father, come home with me now!
    The clock in the steeple strikes three;
   The house is so lonely—the hours are so long
    For poor weeping mother and me.
   Yes, we are alone—poor Benny is dead,
    And gone with the angels of light;
   And these were the very last words that he said—
    'I want to kiss papa, goodnight.'
   Come home, come home, come home,
    Please father, dear father, come home.

CHORUS: Hear the sweet voice of the child, etc.

This is 'Little Mary's Song', by tradition a high spot of the famous Temperance melodrama, *Ten Nights in a Bar-Room*, by William W. Pratt, first performed at the National Theatre, New York, on August 23rd, 1858. Here is part of the scene in which the song appears:

SCENE: *Interior of the 'Sickle and Sheaf'.* JOE MORGAN *is drinking with his friends, including* SIMON SLADE, *the landlord.*

MARY (*outside*). Father! father! where is my father?

Enter MARY—*runs to* MORGAN.

Oh, I've found you, at last! Now won't you come home with me?

MORGAN. Blessings on thee, my little one! Darkly shadowed is the sky that hangs gloomily over thy young head.

MARY. Come, father, mother has been waiting a long time, and I left her crying so sadly. Now do come home, and make us all so happy.

(*The well-known song* 'Father, Dear Father, Come Home with Me Now', *may be introduced with effect.*)

MORGAN. Yes, my child, I'll go. (*Kisses her.*) You have robbed me of my last penny, Simon Slade, but this treasure still remains. Farewell, *friend* Slade, Come, dear one, come. I'll go home! Come, come! I'll go, yes, I'll go! (*Exit* MORGAN *and* MARY.)

Later in the drama a glass is thrown at Morgan, misses him and strikes little Mary on the head. After a fit of delirium tremens for her father, the unfortunate girl passes away while singing a hymn to her distracted parents:

MARY *dies*; MORGAN *falls on the couch.* MRS MORGAN *sobs over the body. Slow music. Tableau.*

There is art in this most apparently artless of songs. The touching melody within the phrase, 'Please, father, dear father, come home,' is cunningly constructed to induce a lump in the throat. The flattened leading note on the word 'dark' provides a neat piece of word-painting, and the 6/8 time signature gives a pleasant impression of childishness. When listening to this ballad one must remember how fresh and forceful it was to its original audiences: these harrowing effects were to become clichés in the hands of equally dedicated if less gifted composers.

Some notes on Henry Clay Work may be found on page 169.

Father's a Drunkard and Mother is Dead

Written by 'STELLA'

Composed by MRS E. A. PARKHURST

1. Out in the gloom-y night, sad-ly I roam, I have no

Father's a Drunkard and Mother is Dead

Mo - ther dear, no pleas-ant home; No-bo-dy cares for me — no one would cry Ev - en if poor lit - tle Bes-sie should die. Bare - foot and tired, I've wan-der'd all day, Ask - ing for work — but I'm too small they say; On the damp ground I must now lay my head — "Fa-ther's a Drunkard, and Mo-ther is dead!"

CHORUS

Mo-ther, oh! why did you leave me a - lone, With

no one to love me, no friends and no home?

Father's a Drunkard and Mother is Dead

255

Father's a Drunkard, and Mother is Dead

1. Out in the gloomy night, sadly I roam,
      I have no Mother dear, no pleasant home;
   Nobody cares for me—no one would cry
      Even if poor little Bessie should die.
   Barefoot and tired, I've wander'd all day,
      Asking for work—but I'm too small they say;
   On the damp ground I must now lay my head—
      'Father's a Drunkard, and Mother is dead!'

CHORUS: Mother, oh! why did you leave me alone,
         With no one to love me, no friends and no home?
         Dark is the night, and the storm rages wild,
         God pity Bessie, the Drunkard's lone child!

2. We were so happy till Father drank rum,
      Then all our sorrow and trouble begun;
   Mother grew paler, and wept ev'ry day,
      Baby and I were too hungry to play.
   Slowly they faded, and one Summer's night
      Found their dear faces all silent and white;
   Then with big tears slowly dropping, I said:
      'Father's a Drunkard, and Mother is dead!'

CHORUS: Mother, oh! why did you leave me alone, etc.

3. Oh! if the 'Temp'rance men' only could find
      Poor, wretched Father, and talk very kind—
   If they could stop him from drinking—why, then
      I should be so very happy again!
   Is it too late? 'men of Temp'rance', please try,
      Or poor little Bessie may soon starve and die.
   All the day long I've been begging for bread—
      'Father's a Drunkard, and Mother is dead!'

CHORUS: Mother, oh! why did you leave me alone, etc.

The sheet-music of this song has the following introduction:

One dismal, stormy night in winter, a little girl—barefooted and miserably clad—leaned shivering against a large tree near the President's House. 'Sissie,' said a passing stranger, 'why don't you go home?'

    She raised her pale face, and with tears dimming her sweet blue eyes, answered mournfully: 'I have no home. Father's a Drunkard, and Mother is Dead.'

There was quite a little school of songs based on remarks overheard in the street. 'Let Me Kiss Him for His Mother' on page 290 is one such, and there is a ballad by C. F. Wood, 'Somebody's Grandpa', about a little girl who defends an old man found drunk on a doorstep: 'She took up her little apron and wiped his face, and then looked up so pitifully . . . and said, "Oh, don't hurt him! He's somebody's grandpa!"'

'Stella' is described on the sheet-music as being 'of Washington'. Mrs Parkhurst was responsible for the words and music of at least one other temperance gem, 'The Drunkard's Child'. The last stanza of this runs:

> Do not be angry now, father,
> Because I tell you this,
> But let me feel upon my brow,
> Once more thy loving kiss;
> And promise me, those lips no more,
> With drink shall be defil'd,
> That, from a life of want and woe,
> Thou'lt save thy weeping child.

Connoisseurs of the lachrymose will appreciate not only the appealing melody but the pregnant rest before the child's last line, 'Father's a drunkard, etc.', just time for the hint of a sob.

Throw Out the Life-Line!

Written and composed by Rev. E. S. Ufford

1. Throw out the Life-Line a - cross the dark wave! There is a bro - ther whom some - one should save; Some - bo - dy's bro - ther! oh, who then will dare To throw out the Life-Line his per - il to share?

Throw Out the Life-Line!

Throw out the Life-Line! Throw out the Life-Line! Some-one is drift-ing a - way__

Throw out the Life-Line! Throw out the Life-Line! Some-one is drift-ing a - way__

Throw out the Life-Line! Throw out the Life-Line! Some-one is drift-ing a - way__

Throw out the Life-Line! Throw out the Life-Line! Some-one is drift-ing a - way__

Throw out the Life-Line! Throw out the Life-Line! Some-one is sink-ing to - day__

Throw out the Life-Line! Throw out the Life-Line! Some-one is sink-ing to - day__

Throw out the Life-Line! Throw out the Life-Line! Some-one is sink-ing to - day__

Throw out the Life-Line! Throw out the Life-Line! Some-one is sink-ing to - day__

Throw Out the Life-Line!

1. Throw out the Life-Line across the dark wave!
    There is a brother whom someone should save;
    Somebody's brother! oh, who then will dare
    To throw out the Life-Line, his peril to share?

CHORUS: Throw out the Life-Line!
        Throw out the Life-Line!
        Someone is drifting away:
        Throw out the Life-Line!
        Throw out the Life-Line!
        Someone is sinking today.

2. Throw out the Life-Line with hand quick and strong;
    Why do you tarry, my brother, so long?
    See—he is sinking; oh, hasten today—
    And out with the Life-Boat! away, then, away!

CHORUS: Throw out the Life-Line! etc.

3. Throw out the Life-Line to danger-fraught men,
    Sinking in anguish where you've never been,
    Winds of temptation and billows of woe
    Will soon hurl them out where the dark waters flow.

CHORUS: Throw out the Life-Line! etc.

4. Soon will the season of rescue be o'er,
    Soon will they drift to eternity's shore;
    Haste then, my brother! no time for delay,
    But throw out the Life-Line, and save them today!

CHORUS: Throw out the Life-Line! etc.

The image of the life of a sailor saved from drowning is apt, if one imagines an ocean comprised of liquor, not brine. This life-saving theme runs right through temperance history. In mid-Victorian England, the Temperance Lifeboat Crews, originating in Staffordshire in 1861, carried the metaphor as far as to dress up as lifeboat men, rather confusingly in Garibaldian costume in honour of the Italian patriot, then at the height of popular British favour. They marched with model boats to protest outside public houses, and the whole business of casting life-lines to drunkards was attended by much procedural mumbo-jumbo in imitation of the freemasons.

This particular song, however, is American, from Ira D. Sankey's *Sacred Songs and Solos*. It is a nicely functional piece of work, typical of Sankey's collection.

Temp'rance Bells

Author and composer unknown

1. Hark! the Temp - 'rance Bells — are — ring - ing, joy - ous
mus - ic fills the air, strength and hope their tones — are —
bring - ing To the homes where dwelt des - pair.

CHORUS

Hear the bells! joy - ous bells! Join the
Hear the bells! joy - ous bells! Join the
Hear the bells! joy - ous bells! Join the
Hear the bells! joy - ous bells! Join the

Temp'rance Bells

1. Hark! the Temp'rance Bells are ringing,
     Joyous music fills the air,
   Strength and hope their tones are
           bringing
     To the homes where dwelt despair.

CHORUS: Hear the Bells! joyous Bells!
          Join the anthem of the free!
          Hear the Bells! merry Bells!
          Sound the Temp'rance Jubilee!

2. Long the tyrant foe hath taken
     Cherish'd lov'd ones for his own,
   Now his cruel power is shaken,
     Soon will fall his tott'ring throne.

CHORUS: Hear the Bells! etc.

3. Brothers come, the hosts are forming,
     Let us join without delay,
   Bright the hills with tints of morning,
     Dawning of a better day.

CHORUS: Hear the Bells! etc.

A really rousing hymn if sung with enthusiasm and conviction (notice the bells ringing in the tenor and bass of the chorus), this was far more likely to convert the wayward than another piece by E. Clympson, published in *Temperance Songs for Elder Children*, a verse and chorus of which run as follows:

Come, let us sing the praises of
A something very nice, now—
A most delicious tasty thing,
I'm sure you'll all agree!
It is not sugar, tarts or buns,
Nor something made with ice, now;
It is not pudding, pie nor sweets,
Not yet a cup of tea.
'Tis cocoa, cocoa, a steaming cup of cocoa;
'Twill warm your hands and cheer your hearts;
    I tell you what I think;
Like cocoa, cocoa, we ought to make life's yoke, oh,
As pleasant, bright, and good for all
    As this delicious drink.

Burnt Cork & Tears

or, Songs of the Minstrels

Massa's in de Cold Ground

Written and composed by Stephen C. Foster

1. Round de meadows am a - ring - ing De dar-key's mourn-ful song,

While de mock-ing bird am sing - ing, Hap-py as de day am long.

Massa's in de Cold Ground

Where de i-vy am a-creep - ing, O'er de gras-sy mound,

Dare old mas-sa am a-sleep - ing, Sleep-ing in de cold, cold ground.

Down in de corn field, Hear dat mourn - ful sound.

All de dar-kies am a weep - ing, Mas-sa's in de cold, cold ground.

Massa's in de Cold Ground

1. Round de meadows am a-ringing
    De darkey's mournful song,
   While de mocking bird am singing,
    Happy as de day am long.
   Where de ivy am a-creeping,
    O'er de grassy mound,
   Dare old massa am a-sleeping,
    Sleeping in de cold, cold ground.
   Down in de cornfield,
    Hear dat mournful sound.
   All de darkies am a-weeping,
    Massa's in de cold, cold ground.

CHORUS: Down in de cornfield,
       Hear dat mournful sound.
       All de darkies am a-weeping,
       Massa's in de cold, cold ground.

2. When de autumn leaves were falling,
    When de days were cold,
   'Twas hard to hear old massa calling,
    Cayse he was so weak and old.
   Now de orange tree am blooming,
    On de sandy shore,
   Now de summer days am coming,
    Massa nebber calls no more.
   Down in de cornfield, etc.

CHORUS: Down in de cornfield, etc.

3. Massa made de darkeys love him,
    Cayse he was so kind,
   Now dey sadly weep above him,
    Mourning cayse he leave dem behind.
   I cannot work before tomorrow,
    Cayse de tear-drop flow,
   I try to drive away my sorrow,
    Pickin' on de old banjo.
   Down in de cornfield, etc.

CHORUS: Down in de cornfield, etc.

It was Stephen Foster's genius to marry the vigour of early Minstrelsy with the refinement of the parlour to produce a style that has proved timeless in its appeal. The few songs of his in this book illustrate the main themes of his remarkable output.

'Massa's in de Cold Ground' of 1852 exhibits the lachrymose side of Foster's talent, a strain that runs constantly through his work. It is present in such plantation songs as 'Uncle Ned' and 'Old Black Joe', and particularly in those songs he wrote specifically for the drawing-room. His first published composition was a genteel parlour ballad, and all through his life disciples of refinement tried to win him over to a higher plane of song than Minstrel melody. In his decline he returned to the lugubrious ballads that his respectable admirers had approved, and he wrote such gloomy pieces as 'Under the Willow She's Weeping', 'Poor Drooping Maiden' and 'Willie, We Have Missed You'.

The Massa of 'Massa's in de Cold Ground' was popularly identified with Judge Rowan of Bardstown, Kentucky, a cousin of the composer's father.

Stephen Collins Foster (1826–1864) was born into a middle-class family at Lawrenceville, near Pittsburgh, Pennsylvania, the son of Colonel William B. Foster. His parents were baffled by his addiction to music, for while his sisters indulged in it with mild pleasure as a polite accomplishment, it could hardly be called a family passion.

With his brother and other boys, young Stephen joined in a 'Thespian Company' to sing plantation songs. He began work as a book-keeper for his brother, but he was already, self-taught, writing songs and was encouraged to become a full-time composer by the prize-winning 'Susanna', written for a musical competition in Pittsburgh for an Ethiopian melody. At first, he was deeply troubled by his success, such were the stifling effects of his background and the current critical disapproval of 'the Ethiopian business'. He was content to omit his name from the sheet-music of his early songs, and at Foster's own request, for the consideration of $15, Edwin P. Christy published 'Old Folks at Home' as 'written and composed by E. P. Christy'. It was the Minstrel impresario, Christy, who brought Foster money and public success, but the composer was hopelessly improvident, often reduced to living on advance royalties for songs yet to be written. His marriage to a doctor's daughter, the heroine of 'Jeanie with the Light-Brown Hair', was a disaster. He sold much of his output for practically nothing to buy liquor, alienating family and friends in the process. Sometimes too impoverished to buy music-paper, he wrote out the words and music of his songs on brown wrapping-paper. Inevitably, his end was tragic: penniless, except for 38 cents, he fainted in a hotel bedroom and accidentally cut his throat on a wash-basin. Two days later, on January 13th, 1864, he was dead.

Foster's enormous appeal has been effectively summed up by Gilbert Chase in *America's Music*. It came from the 'cultural dualism of his background, through which he was able to combine the vitality of the frontier and a certain element of primitive simplicity with the genteel tradition of the urban fringe, dominated by sentimentality, conventionalism, and propriety'. Such was the context, but it was Stephen Foster's astonishing melodic gift that made him a song-writer for all time rather than just for his own period.

'Massa's in de Cold Ground' is, like much of Foster's output, virtually faultless. He seems to have had an instinct for writing perfectly vocal melody which marries utterly with the words. He is probably the most consistently excellent melodist represented in this collection.

My Old Kentucky Home, Goodnight

Written and composed by STEPHEN C. FOSTER

1. The sun shines bright in the old Ken-tuck-y home, 'Tis sum-mer, the dar-kies are gay, The corn top's ripe, and the

mead - ow's in the bloom, While the birds make mu - sic all the

day. The young folks roll on the lit - tle ca - bin floor, All

mer - ry, all hap - py and bright: By'n by hard times comes a -

-knock - ing at the door, Then my old Ken - tuck - y Home, good night.

My Old Kentucky Home, Goodnight

My Old Kentucky Home, Goodnight

1. The sun shines bright in the old Kentucky home,
    'Tis summer, the darkies are gay,
   The corn-top's ripe, and the meadow's in the bloom,
    While the birds make music all the day.
   The young folks roll on the little cabin floor,
    All merry, all happy and bright:
   By'n by hard times comes a-knocking at the door,
    Then my old Kentucky Home, goodnight.

CHORUS: Weep no more, my lady,
    Oh! weep no more today!
   We will sing one song for the old Kentucky Home,
   For the old Kentucky Home far away.

2. They hunt no more for the possum and the coon,
    On the meadow, the hill, and the shore;
   They sing no more, by the glimmer of the moon,
    On the bench by the old cabin door,
   The day goes by like a shadow o'er the heart,
    With sorrow where all was delight.
   The time has come when the darkies have to part,
    Then my old Kentucky Home, goodnight.

CHORUS: Weep no more, my lady, etc.

3. The head must bow, and the back will have to bend,
    Wherever the darkey may go;
   A few more days, and the trouble all will end
    In the field where the sugar-canes grow,
   A few more days for to tote the weary load,
    No matter, 'twill never be light,
   A few more days till we totter on the road,
    Then my old Kentucky Home, goodnight.

CHORUS: Weep no more, my lady.

The supposed location of the old Kentucky home was Federal Hill, the mansion of Judge Rowan, the cousin of Foster's father, at Bardstown, Kentucky. The first draft of the song was entitled, 'Poor Uncle Tom, Goodnight', probably composed under the influence of *Uncle Tom's Cabin*.

The folk-song flavour of this ballad has ensured its continuing popularity. In its time, however, it was its expression of the typical Victorian nostalgia for home, an element it shared with Foster's 'The Old Folks at Home', that was mainly responsible for its immense success. Not only was the composer using an established parlour theme, but the lyric is in plain English and not in mock-Negro dialect, a quality that must have made it even more acceptable in the drawing-room. Despite this, the ballad has a feeling that can only be called ethnic, while being absolutely diatonic and not at all modal. These songs of Foster's do not appear to have been written at all, but rather to have swum up out of a collective musical consciousness and to have melted on to paper.

Beautiful Dreamer

Written and composed by STEPHEN C. FOSTER

1. Beau-ti-ful dream - er, wake un-to me,____ Starlight and dew-drops are wait-ing for thee,____ Sounds of the rude world heard in the day.____ Lull'd by the moon-light have all pass'd a - way!____

Beau - ti - ful dream - er, queen of my song,____ List while I woo thee with

sweet me - lo - dy,____ Gone are the cares of life's bu - sy throng.____

Beau - ti - ful dream - er, a - wake un - to me,____

Beau - ti - ful dream - er, a - wake un - to me.____

a tempo

Beautiful Dreamer

1. Beautiful dreamer, wake unto me,
   Starlight and dew-drops are waiting for thee,
   Sounds of the rude world heard in the day
   Lull'd by the moon-light have all pass'd away!
   Beautiful dreamer, queen of my song,
   List while I woo thee with sweet melody,
   Gone are the cares of life's busy throng.
   Beautiful dreamer, awake unto me,
   Beautiful dreamer, awake unto me.

2. Beautiful dreamer, out on the sea,
   Mermaids are haunting the wild lorelie,
   Over the streamlet vapours are borne,
   Waiting to fade at the bright coming morn,
   Beautiful dreamer, beam on my heart,
   E'en as the morn on the streamlet and sea,
   Then will all clouds of sorrow depart,
   Beautiful dreamer, awake unto me,
   Beautiful dreamer, awake unto me.

'Beautiful Dreamer' was published as Stephen Foster's last song, written only a few days before his death in January 1864. Unhappily for the legend, although it is impossible to establish the exact date of composition, there is evidence that it was in existence at least six months previously. When Foster's death became known several publishers rushed into print with his 'last' songs, some of them probably by other hands.

It is the best song of the composer's final years, a period marked by a sad decline in the quality of his inspiration. With 'Jeanie with the Light-Brown Hair', it represents the best of Foster's gently nostalgic love songs, belonging in manner as much to the parlour as to the Minstrel stage.

Pretty Dinah Snow

Written by M. H. DRUMMOND

Oh,___ dark - ies, give at - ten-tion, And a stor - y I'll re - late, A -

- bout a pret - ty co - lor'd girl In old Ken - tuc - ky state. Oh!___

mourn with me the hap-less fate Of pret-ty Di - nah Snow, She

came to death by drown-ing In the ri - ver O - hi - o.

Pretty Dinah Snow

Pretty Dinah Snow

1. Oh, darkies, give attention,
   And a story I'll relate,
   About a pretty color'd girl
   In old Kentucky state.
   Oh! mourn with me the hapless fate
   Of pretty Dinah Snow,
   She came to death by drowning
   In the river Ohio.

   CHORUS: Oh! my witching Dinah Snow,
   Oh! my witching Dinah Snow,
   She came to death by drowning
   In the river Ohio.

2. 'Twas a dark and dreary night,
   The stormy winds did blow,
   She went on board the horse-boat
   To cross the Ohio.
   The waves ran high and in the deep
   Her graceful form did go,
   The river's cold embrace received
   My pretty Dinah Snow.

   CHORUS: Oh! my witching Dinah Snow,
   etc.

3. The handkerchief that round her head
   That night my Dinah wore,
   Convey'd the sad intelligence,
   'Twas washed up on the shore;
   Her body floated to the sea,
   Her soul to heav'n did go,
   And there I hope again to see
   My pretty Dinah Snow.

   CHORUS: Oh! my witching Dinah Snow,
   etc.

Far more typical of the normal Minstrel fare than Foster's brilliant pieces, 'Pretty Dinah Snow' combines a jaunty, vigorous tune with the most pathetic of lyrics. It lacks the Foster fire but still has great appeal.

The Yellow Rose of Texas

Written and composed by J.K.

Allegretto

mf

p

1. There's a yel-low rose in Tex-as That I am going to see, No

o – ther dar – key knows her, No dar – key on – ly me; She

cried so when I left her. It like to broke my heart, And

if I ev - er find— her, We nev - er-more will part.

CHORUS

She's the sweet-est rose of co-lour This dar-key ev - er knew, Her

She's the sweet-est rose of co-lour This dar-key ev - er knew, Her

She's the sweet-est rose of co-lour This dar-key ev - er knew, Her

p staccato

eyes are bright as dia-monds, They spar-kle like the dew; You may

eyes are bright as dia-monds, They spar-kle like the dew; You may

eyes are bright as dia-monds, They spar-kle like the dew; You may

The Yellow Rose of Texas

talk a - bout your dear - est May, And sing of Ro - sa Lee, But the

talk a - bout your dear - est May, And sing of Ro - sa Lee, But the

talk a - bout your dear - est May, And sing of Ro - sa Lee, But the

yel - low rose of Tex - as Beats the belles of Ten - nes - see.

yel - low rose of Tex - as Beats the belles of Ten - nes - see.

yel - low rose of Tex - as Beats the belles of Ten - nes - see.

mf

The Yellow Rose of Texas

1. There's a yellow rose in Texas
      That I am going to see,
   No other darkey knows her,
      No darkey only me;
   She cried so when I left her,
      It like to broke my heart,
   And if I ever find her,
      We never more will part.

CHORUS: She's the sweetest rose of color
         This darkey ever knew,
      Her eyes are bright as diamonds,
         They sparkle like the dew;
      You may talk about your dearest May,
         And sing of Rosa Lee,
      But the yellow rose of Texas
         Beats the belles of Tennessee.

2. Where the Rio Grande is flowing,
      And the starry skies are bright,
   She walks along the river,
      In the quiet summer night;
   She thinks, if I remember,
      When we parted long ago,
   I promis'd to come back again,
      And not to leave her so.

CHORUS: She's the sweetest rose of
         color, etc.

3. Oh! now I'm going to find her,
      For my heart is full of woe,
   And we'll sing the song together,
      That we sung so long ago;
   We'll play the banjo gaily,
      And we'll sing the songs of yore,
   And the yellow rose of Texas
      Shall be mine for evermore.

CHORUS: She's the sweetest rose of
         color, etc.

The author and composer of this famous song has never been identified. It was published in New York City in 1858. Like 'Dixie's Land' it has transcended its origins on the Minstrel stage to become a piece of international celebrity.

Dixie's Land

Written and composed by DANIEL D. EMMETT

1. I wish I was in de land ob cot-ton, Old times dar am not for-got-ten, To de land, to de land, to de land, to de land. In Dix-ie's land, whar I was born in, Ear-ly on one fros-ty mornin', To de land, to de land, to de land, to de

Dixie's Land

1. I wish I was in de land ob cotton,
   Old times dar am not forgotten,
     To de land, to de land, to de land, to de land.
   In Dixie's land, whar I was born in,
   Early on one frosty mornin',
     To de land, to de land, to de land, to de land,
     Den I wish I was in Dixie.

CHORUS: Oh! in Dixie's land I'll take my stand,
         And lib and die in Dixie.
         Away, away, away down souf in Dixie.
         Away, away, away down souf in Dixie.

2. Old missus marry 'Will de weaber',
   Willium was a gay deceaber,
     To de land, to de land, to de land, to de land.
   But when he put his arm around her,
   He smiled as fierce as a forty pounder,
     To de land, to de land, to de land, to de land,
     Den I wish I was in Dixie.

CHORUS: Oh! in Dixie's land I'll take my stand, etc.

3. His face was sharp as a butcher's cleaber,
   But dat did not seem to grieb her,
     To de land, to de land, to de land, to de land.
   Old Missus acted de foolish part,
   And died for a man dat broke her heart,
     To de land, to de land, to de land, to de land,
     Den I wish I was in Dixie.

CHORUS: Oh! in Dixie's land I'll take my stand, etc.

4. Now here's a health to next old Missus,
   An' all de gals dat want to kiss us,
     To de land, to de land, to de land, to de land.
   But if you want to drive away sorrow,
   Come and hear dis song tomorrow,
     To de land, to de land, to de land, to de land,
     Den I wish I was in Dixie.

CHORUS: Oh! in Dixie's land I'll take my stand, etc.

5. Dar's buckwheat cake an' Ingen batter,
   Makes you fat or a little fatter,
     To de land, to de land, to de land, to de land.
   Den how it down an' scratch your grabble,
   To Dixie's land I'm bound to trabble,
     To de land, to de land, to de land, to de land,
     Den I wish I was in Dixie.

CHORUS: Oh! in Dixie's land I'll take my stand, etc.

Known throughout the world as a song of the American South, a song that can still revive old loyalties and old hatreds, 'Dixie' began life in fact as 'Dixie's Land', a 'walk-around' written by a black-face Minstrel with Unionist sympathies. It was born in a boarding-house in New York City on a wet November Sunday in 1859. Dan Emmett, a principal member of Bryant's Minstrels, had to write a new piece for the climax of their show the next night, and the doggerel of his words and the fierce perkiness of his music coalesced into the song that swept the nation.

Much has been written on the origin of the term 'Dixie'. The first recorded use of the word in print occurs in 1850: it was the name of a Negro character in a Minstrel play. Emmett himself mentioned 'Dixie's land' in a song written earlier in 1859. It could be that 'Dixie' was a common Minstrel name for a comic Negro, and his land would naturally be the South, but there are at least four other theories about the origin of the word. Perhaps the most convincing is that 'Dixie' was used by the Northern circus troupes, of which Emmett was for some years a member. The South to them was all routes below Mason and Dixon's line, and as the cold weather approached and the troupes headed South they looked forward to arriving in the comforting warmth of 'Dixie'. Another suggestion finds an origin in the pre-Civil War ten-dollar bills printed in French by a Louisiana bank, with a large DIX for ten on the face. These Southern bills were naturally nicknamed 'Dixies' and the South would have been the 'Dixies' land'. There is no evidence of this usage, however. A more fanciful theory links 'Dixie' with the name of an eighteenth-century slave-holder on Manhattan Island, reputed to be so kind to his Negroes that when sold away they pined for the old days in 'Dixie's land'. Eventually, folk memory transferred that golden land down South. Again, no evidence has been found to support this idea. There is also a conjecture that 'Dixie's Land' was a phrase used in the children's game 'Tom Tiddler's Ground' in New York before the Civil War, but if this was so the term could well have come from the Minstrel stage.

'Dixie's Land' became wildly popular and in the next few years dozens of versions appeared. Rival and often bellicose lyrics were written to laud the North or the South depending upon the persuasion of the plagiarist. Contrary to popular belief, it was still a favourite in the North and with Union troops at least until 1863, but the South finally and irretrievably annexed it as a battle hymn. Dan Emmett had strong feelings for the Negro and for abolition, and is reported to have remarked with some asperity, when told by a Ministrel friend that it could be heard across the front line being played by Confederate bands, 'Yes: and if I had known what use they were going to put my song, I will be damned if I'd have written it.' His actual remuneration for the copyright was $500, but Emmett lived on the reputation for having written it right into old age.

A few days before his assassination, President Lincoln made a speech at the White House, which he concluded by saying: 'I see you have a band with you I should like to hear it play "Dixie". I have consulted the Attorney General, who is here by my side, and he is of the opinion that "Dixie" belongs to us. Now play it.'

Daniel Decatur Emmett ('Old Dan Emmett', 1818–1904) was a key figure in Negro Minstrelsy, both as performer and composer. He danced, sang, fiddled and played the banjo; he wrote music, lyrics, stump speeches, sketches and plays; 'Old Dan Tucker' and 'The Blue-Tailed Fly' are ascribed to him. Born into a pioneer family of Mount Vernon, Ohio, he first worked for a printer, but he left home at eighteen to join the army, giving his age as twenty-one. Until the authorities found him out and discharged him, his musical talents earned him the appointment of 'leading fifer' and drummer. Then he worked alternately as printer and musician in a circus troupe, writing his first Minstrel song, performed in black-face on the back of a horse, in 1844. He was soon appearing in the ring and toured as a musician for several circuses, moving over to a career as a Minstrel performer. He was a founder-member of the first real Minstrel band, the Virginia Minstrels, and after touring with them in England returned to America to form more troupes, appear in others and occasionally perform once more in the circus ring. In 1858 he joined one of the best of all the companies, Bryant's Minstrels, for whom he wrote 'Dixie'. On leaving them, his career was one of slow and sad decline. He lost his voice, became a fiddler, wrote comic sermons for a newspaper and opened a saloon. Friends organised benefits for him, and he joined in a travelling revival of old-time Minstrelsy in his eighties, raising the roof every time he sang his famous song. Finally he retired to a small cottage near his birthplace at Mount Vernon, where he spent his last years genially, supported by a pension from the Actors' Fund of America, savouring his celebrity as composer of one of his nation's greatest songs.

The version of 'Dixie's Land' printed here is not the earliest. It is, however, the one best known. The original manuscript has as its second line, 'Cimmon seed an' sandy bottom', and instead of 'To de land' had 'Look away' as the chorus in the verse. At the opening of the full chorus, the original had, instead of the long 'Oh! . . .', 'Hooray! Hooray!' followed by the line, 'In Dixie's land, I'll took my stand'. There are other, minor variations, too.

As originally performed, the song sounded rather differently from what we enjoy today. In his fascinating *Dan Emmett and the Rise of Early Negro Minstrelsy*, Dr Hans Nathan described how it must have struck its auditors:

> . . . its original tempo . . . was considerably slower than the one now preferred by military bands. The tune is characterised by a heavy, nonchalant, inelegant strut . . . If music, lyrics, and dance style are taken as an entity, there emerges a special kind of humour that mixes grotesqueness with lustiness and down-to-earth contentment—comparable, to overstate the case, to a blend of Breughel and Mickey Mouse.

Let Me Kiss Him for His Mother

Written by JOHN P. ORDWAY

Composed by L. O. EMERSON

Let Me Kiss Him for His Mother

love him for his mo-ther, And seek her bless-ing now. Kind friends have sooth'd his pil-low, Have watch'd his ev' - ry care; Be - neath the weep - ing wil-low, O lay him gen - tly there.

Let Me Kiss Him for His Mother

1. Let me kiss him for his mother,
    Let me kiss his youthful brow;
I will love him for his mother,
    And seek her blessing now.
Kind friends have sooth'd his pillow,
    Have watch'd his ev'ry care;
Beneath the weeping willow,
    O lay him gently there.

CHORUS: Sleep, dearest, sleep,
            I love you as a brother,
            Kind friends around you weep,
            I've kiss'd you for your mother.

2. Let me kiss him for his mother,
    What tho' left a stranger here;
She has lov'd him as none other,
    I feel her blessing near.
Tho' cold that form lies sleeping,
    He wears an angel's crown;
Dear friends around are weeping,
    O lay him gently down.

CHORUS: Sleep, dearest, sleep, etc.

3. Let me kiss him for his mother,
    Or perchance a sister dear;
If a father or a brother,
    I feel their blessing here.
Then kiss him for his mother,
    'Twill soothe her after years;
Farewell, dear stranger brother,
    Our requiem our tears.

CHORUS: Sleep, dearest, sleep, etc.

The following note was appended to the original edition of this song: 'The verses of this ballad were suggested by a touching incident which is said to have occurred at New Orleans during a dreadful fever season. A young man, who had died there, lonely and a stranger, was about to be carried to the grave when a lady passed to the coffin and pressed her lips to his forehead, saying, "Let me kiss him for his mother." '

John P. Ordway wrote and published his own songs—this one dates from 1859—and Luther Orlando Emerson was a composer also responsible for the famous setting of 'We are Coming, Father Abraham' and the music of the hymn 'Stand Up for Jesus'.

An example of the strong lugubrious element in the black-face repertoire, this favourite of the Christy Minstrels forms an apt prelude to the next section.

Lilies & Crape

or, Songs of Disaster and Death

The Death of Nelson

Written by S. J. ARNOLD

Composed by JOHN BRAHAM

O'er Nel - son's Tomb, with si - lent grief op -

- press'd, Bri - tan - nia mourns her He - ro, now at rest: But those bright

lau - rels   ne'er shall fade with   years,   Whose leaves, whose leaves are

wa - ter'd   by a Na-tions tears.

ARIA
Allegro

'Twas__ in Tra-fal - gar's   bay   We

The Death of Nelson

beau-ty,   A - long the line this   sig - nal   ran,   Eng - land ex-

-pects   that ev' - ry man   This day will_ do his_ du-ty!   This

day   will _____ do   his _____ du-ty!

ff

And_ now   the Can - nons

roar   A - long th' af -fright-ed   shore,   Our Nel - son_ led   the_

ff

way,   His   Ship   the   Vic - t'ry   nam'd!

Long   be   that   Vic - to - ry   fam'd,   For __   Vic - t'ry __ crown'd   the __

day!   But   dear - ly   was   that   con - quest   bought,

Too   well   the   gal - lant   He - ro   fought,   For   Eng - land,   home __   and

beau - ty,   For __   Eng - land   home __   and   beau - ty.   He

The Death of Nelson

cried as 'midst the fire he ran, "Eng - land shall find that ev' — ry man, This day will do his du –ty! This day will do his du-ty!"

At last the fa-tal wound, Which spread dis-may a - round, The

He - ro's breast, the ____ He - ro's breast re - ceiv'd;

"Heav'n fights on our - side, The day's our own," he cried! "Now ____

long e - nough I've ____ liv'd! In hon - or's cause my life was past, In

hon - or's cause I fall at last, For Eng - land home ____ and.

beau - ty, For Eng - land home ____ and beau-ty." Thus

end - ing life as he be - gan, Eng - land con -fess'd that

ev' - ry man, That day had_done his_ du -ty, That

day had____ done his____ du -ty!

The Death of Nelson

RECITATIVE: O'er Nelson's Tomb, with silent grief oppress'd,
Britannia mourns her Hero, now at rest:
But those bright laurels ne'er shall fade with years,
Whose leaves, whose leaves are water'd by a Nation's tears.

ARIA: 'Twas in Trafalgar's bay
We saw the Frenchmen lay,
    Each heart was bounding then,
We scorn'd the foreign yoke,
For our Ships were British Oak,
    And hearts of oak our men!
Our Nelson mark'd them on the wave,
Three cheers our gallant Seamen gave,
    Nor thought of home or beauty,
    Nor thought of home or beauty,
Along the line this signal ran,
England expects that ev'ry man
    This day will do his duty!
    This day will do his duty!

And now the Cannons roar
Along th'affrighted shore,
    Our Nelson led the way,
His Ship the Vict'ry nam'd!
Long be that Victory fam'd,
    For Vict'ry crown'd the day!
But dearly was that conquest bought,
Too well the gallant Hero fought,
    For England, home and beauty,
    For England, home and beauty.
He cried as 'midst the fire he ran,
'England shall find that ev'ry man,
    This day will do his duty!
    This day will do his duty!'

At last the fatal wound,
Which spread dismay around,
    The Hero's breast, the Hero's breast receiv'd;
'Heav'n fights on our side,
The day's our own,' he cried!
    'Now long enough I've liv'd!
In honor's cause my life was past,
In honor's cause I fall at last,
    For England, home and beauty,
    For England, home and beauty.'
Thus ending life as he began,
England confess'd that ev'ry man,
    That day had done his duty,
    That day had done his duty!

The great exhibition piece for Victorian tenors, this song was first performed as part of the opera, *The Americans*, in 1811. It was certainly very effective upon occasion. Once, its composer, the tenor, John Braham, was in full spate when Emma, Lady Hamilton, who was in the audience in a private box, was taken ill. 'Before the second verse was finished,' it is reported, 'sobs and screams were heard ringing through the theatre.'

It may be that Lady Hamilton was commenting upon the quality of the musical setting, which is unimpressive. A succession of clichés, of mingled pomp, recitativo, jigging tunes and military flourishes, it is witness to the composer's patriotism rather than his inspiration. It is, however, a fine vehicle for the dramatic tenor.

Amateurs, though, should be warned against overdoing the drama. At one concert at the Albert Hall, recalled by the accompanist, Henry Bird, an erstwhile amateur was making his professional debut, boasting that he would perform with more intelligence than was customarily shown by ordinary singers. He said that in the last verse he would impersonate Nelson's dying moments with full realism. On stage he gasped out the words, 'In honour's cause my life was passed,' with a long pause between each syllable, reducing the audience to the wrong kind of tears. His professional career was stillborn.

The lyricist, Samuel James Arnold, was the son of the opera composer, Dr Arnold. Fond of nautical subjects, he also wrote the musical dramas *The Shipwreck* and *The Veteran Tar*. He was also the original author of 'A Life on the Ocean Wave' (see page 105). As well as an author, Arnold was a portrait painter who exhibited at the Royal Academy.

John Braham (1774–1856) was England's most famous tenor until the coming of Sims Reeves. Of Jewish origin (his original name was Abraham), he was reputed to have been excessively interested in business from his earliest years. As a boy he had a very sweet voice, and a gentleman staying in the house asked him to sing. The young Braham demanded sixpence for a song. 'Can't you make it less?' 'Not for one,' replied the boy, 'but I'll sing you three for a shilling.' He first appeared in public at Covent Garden at the age of thirteen, and grew up, as Planché remarked, into 'the greatest English tenor perhaps ever known', but 'perhaps the worst actor ever seen, and the most unromantic person in appearance that can well be imagined'. Short, thick, with a scrubby light-brown wig, Braham was none the less transformed as soon as he began to sing, although he was frequently criticised for playing to the gallery in his choice of popular but meretricious music. He sang in opera houses all over Europe, delighting Napoleon (not, one assumes, with 'The Death of Nelson'), and had a sensationally successful tour of America in 1836. In later years he lost the huge fortune he had made in unwise speculations, and, his voice failing, he was forced to travel the provinces in concert enterprises with his sons.

The Snow Storm

Written by SEBA SMITH

Composed by LYMAN HEATH

cold   wind swept   the moun - tain's height,   And path - less was   the

306

The Snow Storm

drea - ry wild, And 'mid the cheer - less hours of night A mo-ther wan - dered with her child; As through the drift - ed snows she pressed, The babe was sleep - ing on her breast, The babe was sleep-ing on her breast.

dolce

espress.

D.S.

The Snow Storm

1. The cold wind swept the mountain's height,
   And pathless was the dreary wild,
   And 'mid the cheerless hours of night
   A mother wandered with her child;
   As through the drifted snows she pressed,
   The babe was sleeping on her breast,
   The babe was sleeping on her breast.

2. And colder still the winds did blow,
   And darker hours of night came on,
   And deeper grew the drifts of snow—
   Her limbs were chilled, her strength was gone:
   'O God!' she cried, in accents wild,
   'If I must perish, save my child,
   If I must perish, save my child!'

3. She stript her mantle from her breast,
   And bared her bosom to the storm;
   As round the child she wrapped the vest,
   She smiled to think that it was warm.
   With one cold kiss, one tear she shed,
   And sunk upon a snowy bed,
   And sunk upon a snowy bed.

4. At dawn, a traveller passed by,
   And saw her 'neath a snowy veil—
   The frost of death was in her eye,
   Her cheek was cold, and hard, and pale—
   He moved the robe from off the child;
   The babe looked up, and sweetly smiled,
   The babe looked up, and sweetly smiled.

This was one of the highly dramatic songs popularised in the United States by the Hutchinson family.

Seba Smith (1792–1868) started out life as a teacher, but settled down as a journalist and humorist in Portland, Maine, where he founded the Portland *Courier*. His great claim to fame was the series of political dialect letters published under the name of 'Major Jack Downing', which were widely imitated. 'Downing' even ended up in stage version in New York. Seba Smith had a poetical wife of some note, Elizabeth Oakes Smith.

Lyman Heath (1804–1870) composed a number of other songs, including 'The Cot Where I was Born' and 'The Grave of Bonaparte'. He was also a singer, and came from Nashua, New Hampshire. 'The Snow Storm' alas, despite its popularity, is no great tribute to his genius. There is, seek as one may, no melody. The arpeggios appear to represent the snow storm, but when they stop briefly for what appears to be a pregnant two bars there is nothing particularly momentous in the text. There is no great help for the singer, either, but then its original interpreters were robust enough to do without it.

Ring the Bell Softly

Written by W. D. Smith

Composed by E. N. Catlin

1. Some-one has gone from this strange world of ours, No more to ga-ther its thorns with its flow - ers, No more to lin - ger where sun-beams must fade, Where, on all beau - ty death's fin – gers are

309

laid; Wea – ry with ming – ling life's bit – ter and

sweet, Wea – ry with part – ing and ne – ver to

meet, Some – one has gone to the bright gold – en

shore, Ring the bell soft – ly there's crape on the

door, Ring the bell soft – ly there's crape on the door.

Ring the Bell Softly

Weary with mingling life's bitter and sweet, Weary with parting and never to meet, Someone has gone to the

bright gold - en shore, Ring the bell soft - ly, there's crape on the

bright gold - en shore, Ring the bell soft - ly, there's crape on the

bright gold - en shore, Ring the bell soft - ly, there's crape on the

bright gold - en shore, Ring the bell soft - ly, there's crape on the

door, Ring the bell soft - ly, there's crape on the door.

door, Ring the bell soft - ly, there's crape on the door.

door, Ring the bell soft - ly, there's crape on the door.

door, Ring the bell soft - ly, there's crape on the door.

Ring the Bell Softly

1. Someone has gone from this strange world of ours,
     No more to gather its thorns with its flowers,
  No more to linger where sunbeams must fade,
     Where, on all beauty death's fingers are laid;
  Weary with mingling life's bitter and sweet,
     Weary with parting and never to meet,
  Someone has gone to the bright golden shore,
     Ring the bell softly, there's crape on the door.

CHORUS: Weary with mingling life's bitter and sweet,
              Weary with parting and never to meet,
              Someone has gone to the bright golden shore,
              Ring the bell softly, there's crape on the door,
              Ring the bell softly, there's crape on the door.

2. Someone is resting from sorrow and sin,
     Happy where earth's conflicts enter not in;
  Joyous as birds when the morning is bright,
     When the sweet sunbeams have brought us their light;
  Weary with sowing and never to reap,
     Weary with labour and welcoming sleep,
  Someone's departed to heaven's glad shore,
     Ring the bell softly, there's crape on the door.

CHORUS: Weary with mingling life's bitter and sweet, etc.

3. Angels were anxiously longing to meet
     One who walks with them in heaven's bright street;
  Lov'd ones have whisper'd that someone is blest,
     Free from earth's trials, and taking sweet rest;
  Yes! there is one more in angelic bliss,
     One less to cherish and one less to kiss,
  Someone's departed to heaven's bright shore,
     Ring the bell softly, there's crape on the door.

CHORUS: Weary with mingling life's bitter and sweet, etc.

This Minstrel ballad exhibits very clearly the enormous relish the Victorian middle class found in the contemplation of death. Such wallowing in morbidity can only be paralleled by the twentieth century's obsession with sex. The main difference lies in the Victorian belief that the enjoyment of death was essentially improving.

The theme should not be allowed to discourage performance. There is a good melody and chorus magnificent in its musical restraint, only breaking out once in the high G and then remembering itself and decorum in the piano of the last bar.

Dear Mother, I've Come Home to Die

Written by E. BOWERS

Composed by HENRY TUCKER

Dear Mo - ther, I re-mem-ber well The part - ing kiss you gave to me, When mer - ry rang the vil - lage bell —— My

314

Dear Mother, I've Come Home to Die

heart was full of joy and glee; I did not dream that one short

sempre legato

ritard.

year Would crush the hopes that soar'd so high! Oh,

ritard.

Con molto espressione *ritard.*

Mo - ther dear, draw near to me, Dear Mo-ther, I've come home to die.

ritard. *colla voce*

CHORUS

Call Sis - ter, Bro - ther, to my side, And

Call Sis - ter, Bro - ther, to my side, And

Call Sis - ter, Bro - ther, to my side, And

Call Sis - ter, Bro - ther, to my side, And

Dear Mother, I've Come Home to Die

1. Dear Mother, I remember well
      The parting kiss you gave to me,
   When merry rang the village bell—
      My heart was full of joy and glee;
   I did not dream that one short year
      Would crush the hopes that soar'd so high!
   Oh, Mother dear, draw near to me,
      Dear Mother, I've come home to die.

   CHORUS: Call Sister, Brother, to my side,
                And take your soldier's last goodbye;
                Oh, Mother dear, draw near to me,
                Dear Mother, I've come home to die.

2. Hark! Mother, 'tis the village bell,
      I can no longer with thee stay:
   My Country calls to Arms, to Arms!
      The foe advance in fierce array!
   The vision's past—I feel that now,
      For Country I can only sigh,
   Oh, Mother dear, draw near to me,
      Dear Mother, I've come home to die.

   CHORUS: Call Sister, Brother, to my side, etc.

3. Dear Mother, Sister, Brother, all,
      One parting kiss to all goodbye;
   Weep not, but clasp your hand in mine,
      And let me like a soldier die!
   I've met the foe upon the field
      Where kindred fiercely did defy,
   I fought for Right—God bless the Flag!
      Dear Mother, I've come home to die.

   CHORUS: Call Sister, Brother, to my side, etc.

E. Bowers wrote many lyrics for the Minstrels; one of them, for Bryant's troupe, was 'How Are You Greenbacks?', written when paper money without the backing of gold was flooding America.

Henry Tucker was active as a composer for over forty years, and produced many favourite sentimental ballads for the Christy Minstrels, among them 'Sweet Genevieve' and 'Weeping, Sad and Lonely' (on page 83). One might guess Tucker's other musical talent from 'Dear Mother': he also composed hymns. He died in Brooklyn in 1882.

The Vacant Chair

Written by HENRY S. WASHBURN

Composed by DR GEORGE F. ROOT

1. We shall meet, but we shall miss him, There will be one va-cant chair; We shall lin-ger to car-ess him, While we breathe our ev'n-ing

The Vacant Chair

prayer; When, a year a-go we ga-thered, Joy was in his mild, blue eye, But a gold-en cord is se-vered, And our hopes in ru-in lie.

REFRAIN

We shall meet, but we shall miss him, There will be one va-cant chair; We shall lin-ger to car-ess him, When we breathe our ev'-ning prayer.

D.C.

The Vacant Chair

1. We shall meet, but we shall miss him,
     There will be one vacant chair;
   We shall linger to caress him,
     While we breathe our ev'ning prayer;
   When, a year ago we gathered,
     Joy was in his mild, blue eye,
   But a golden cord is severed,
     And our hopes in ruin lie.

   REFRAIN: We shall meet, but we shall miss him,
                There will be one vacant chair;
              We shall linger to caress him,
                When we breathe our ev'ning prayer.

2. At our fireside, sad and lonely,
     Often will the bosom swell,
   At remembrance of the story,
     How our noble Willie fell;
   How he strove to bear our banner
     Through the thickest of the fight,
   And uphold our country's honour,
     In the strength of manhood's might.

   REFRAIN: We shall meet, but we shall miss him, etc.

3. True, they tell us wreaths of glory
     Evermore will deck his brow,
   But this soothes the anguish only
     Sweeping o'er our heart-strings now.
   Sleep today, O early fallen!
     In thy green and narrow bed,
   Dirges from the pine and cypress,
     Mingle with the tears we shed.

   REFRAIN: We shall meet, but we shall miss him, etc.

This song commemorates the death of a lieutenant in the 15th Massachusetts Infantry.

Chairs seem to have awakened Victorian emotions with remarkable frequency, almost as often as did grandfather clocks. As well as this touching piece, there is the well-known setting by Henry Russell of Eliza Cook's poem, 'The Old Arm-Chair':

> I love it! I love it! And who shall dare
> To chide me for loving that old arm-chair?

and there is also an effusion by Edward Fitzball with music by Balfe:

> In this old chair my father sat,
> In this my mother smil'd . . .

Henry Washburn was also noted as author of another favoured ballad, 'The Grave of Bonaparte'.

Dr George Frederick Root (1820–1896) was reckoned a century ago America's foremost composer of military songs, many of which cheered the Union troops during the Civil War. The most celebrated of these were 'The Battle Cry of Freedom' ('Rally Round the Flag, Boys!'), 'Just Before the Battle, Mother' and 'Tramp, Tramp, Tramp, the Boys are Marching'. Root opened a Musical Institute in New York City in 1853, but moved to Chicago in the 'sixties to become an editor for his brother's firm of music publishers, Root and Cady. Jealous of the fashionable vogue for German composers of parlour balladry, he brought out some of his songs under a literal translation of his name, Friedrich G. Wurzel. A proponent of the 'better music' movement that hailed from Boston, Root composed a number of appropriately genteel hymns and also cantatas, one of them on the theme of the Pilgrim Fathers.

In 'The Vacant Chair' Dr Root pulled out all the sentimental stops. The sobs are almost audible: 'We shall meet (pause), but we shall miss him (pause), There will be (pause) one vacant chair, etc.' A fine effect, but it is not improved by its prolongation through the rest of the song. A good performance, none the less, can certainly overcome these minor problems and induce the sobs among the audience.

The Pardon Came Too Late

Written and composed by PAUL DRESSER

1. A fair-haired boy in a for-eign land At sun-rise was to die;___ In a pris-on cell he sat a-lone, From his heart there came a sigh,___ De-sert-ed from the ranks, they said, The

322

The Pardon Came Too Late

rea - son none could say;___ They on - ly knew the or - ders were That

he should die next day.___ And as the hours glided by,___ A

mes - sen-ger on wings did fly,___ To save this boy from such a

fate,___ A par - don, but it came too late!___

CHORUS

The vol-ley was fired - at sun-rise, Just after break of day,____ And while the echoes lin-ger'd, A soul had pass'd a - way;____ In- to the arms of his Ma - ker, And there to hear his fate,____ A tear, a sigh, a sad good - bye! The par-don came too late!____

The Pardon Came Too Late

1. A fair-haired boy in a foreign land
     At sunrise was to die;
   In a prison cell he sat alone,
     From his heart there came a sigh,
   Deserted from the ranks, they said,
     The reason none could say;
   They only knew the orders were
     That he should die next day.
   And as the hours glided by,
     A messenger on wings did fly,
   To save this boy from such a fate,
     A pardon, but it came too late!

CHORUS: The volley was fired at sunrise,
          Just after break of day,
          and while the echoes linger'd,
          A soul had pass'd away;
          Into the arms of his Maker,
          And there to hear his fate,
          A tear, a sigh, a sad goodbye!
          The pardon came too late!

2. And 'round the camp fire burning bright,
     The story then was told;
   How his mother on a dying bed,
     Called for her son so bold,
   He hastened to obey her wish,
     Was captured on the way;
   She never saw her boy so fair,
     He died at break of day.
   And when the truth at last was known,
     His innocence at once was shown;
   To save from such an unjust fate,
     A pardon sent, but 'twas too late!

CHORUS: The volley was fired at sunrise,
          etc.

A similar tragedy is narrated in 'The Deserter', a poem by Bayard Taylor, reprinted in *Parlour Poetry*. On that particular occasion, the unfortunate hero dreamed of his wife being murdered by the Comanche Indians, and galloped off. After trial he was generously offered a pardon but was too proud to accept it.

Paul Dresser (1857–1906) was born at Terre Haute, Indiana, on the banks of the Wabash. His real name was Dreiser and his brother achieved fame as the novelist, Theodore Dreiser. Paul ran away from home as a boy, and ended up as an end man in black-face Minstrelsy. He also wrote plays and humorous newspaper pieces. His songs made him famous, especially 'On the Banks of the Wabash'. Most of them were promoters of the damp handkerchief, and they included 'My Gal Sal', 'Just Tell Them That You Saw Me' (which, when he was singing it to his brother, reduced the composer to floods of tears) and, written in 1891, the same year as 'The Pardon Came Too Late', 'Her Tears Drifted Out with the Tide'. Dresser was of enormous bulk with a heart as great as his physique. The most generous denizen of Tin Pan Alley, he wasted much of his money on loans that were never repaid, and eventually reduced himself to penury. At one time, with his jokes and stories, he had been the life and soul of New York barrooms; in his decline his fair-weather friends left him and he died, it is said, of a broken heart. There is a monument to him in Indiana. Naturally it stands on the banks of the Wabash.

Sweet & Low

or, Songs for Several Voices

Come, Let Us Join the Roundelay

Composed by WILLIAM BEALE

Come, Let Us Join the Roundelay

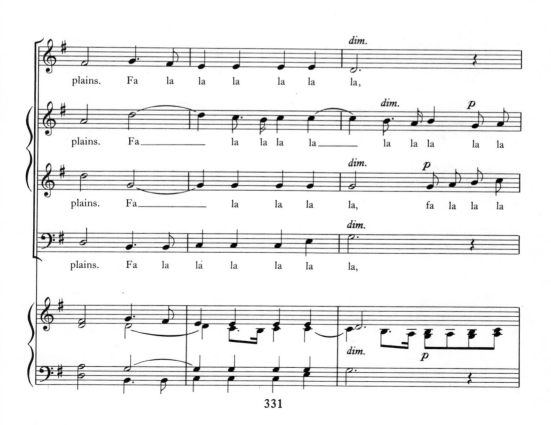

Come, Let Us Join the Roundelay

Come, Let us Join the Roundelay

Come, Let Us Join the Roundelay

Come, let us join the roundelay,
And sing the jocund time away,
Fa la la la, etc.
While the fauns and satyrs round
Dance along on fairy ground,
And the merry nymphs and swains
Gaily trip these rural plains.
Fa la la la, etc.

Here is the musical equivalent of the architecture of the Gothic Revival: the language comes from the past, but the accent is unmistakably nineteenth century.

Madrigals like this example were the product of the Madrigal Society. Founded in 1741 by John Immyns, its purpose was to promote and perform the music of the Golden Age and the periods following. In 1813, the Society offered a handsome silver cup worth ten guineas 'for the best madrigal in not less than four not more than six parts . . . after the manner of the madrigals by Bennet, Wilbye, Morley, Weelkes, Ward, Marenzio and others'. It was carried off by William Beale with 'Awake, Sweet Muse'.

His 'Come, Let Us Join the Roundelay', which had immense popularity, exhibits all the outward signs of its models—imitation, rhythmical freedom (the minims in the 3/2 bars should be read as crotchets, or perhaps dotted crotchets) and new musical ideas for new poetical ones. A closer inspection of the harmony, however, indicates firmly its birth in a later century.

Among the Presidents of the Madrigal Society were Stainer and Sullivan, but neither managed to capture in their madrigals quite the spirit of the originals as had Beale.

William Beale (1787–1854) began his musical education early, as a chorister at Westminster Abbey. When his voice broke he joined the Navy, serving as midshipman on board H.M.S. *Révolutionnaire*, which had been captured from the French. Between 1816 and 1820 he was a gentleman of the Chapel Royal and was well acquainted with the polyphonic repertoire of the English Rite. Most of his musical works consisted of part songs and anthems.

Excelsior!

DUET

Written by H. W. LONGFELLOW

Composed by M. W. BALFE

1. The shades of night were fall-ing fast, As thro' an Al-pine vil-lage pass'd A youth, who bore 'mid snow and ice A ban - ner, with the strange de-vice, "Ex-cel-si - or! Ex-cel - si - or!" 2. His brow was

sad, his eye be-neath Flash'd like a fal-chion from its sheath,

And like a sil-ver clar-ion rung The ac - cents of that

un known tongue, "Ex-cel-si - or! Ex-cel - si - or!" 3. In hap py

homes he saw the light Of house-hold fires gleam warm and bright,

A-bove, the spec-tral glac-iers shone, And from ____ his lips es -

Excelsior!

339

Excelsior!

ware the aw - ful a - va - lanche," This was the pea-sant's

last good-night; A voice re-plied, far up the height,

ppp TENOR   *sempre pianissimo*

"Ex - cel - si - or! "Ex - cel - si -

Ex - cel - si - or!

ppp

riten.

- or! Ex - cel - si - or!

Ex - cel - si - or!

Excelsior!

San Ber-nard Ut-ter'd an oft - re -peat-ed pray'r,

San Ber-nard Ut-ter'd an oft re -peat-ed pray'r, A

A voice cried___ thro' the

voice cried___ thro' the start -led air, A voice cried___ thro' the

start - led air, "Ex -cel -si - or! Ex -cel - si - or!"

start - led air, "Ex -cel -si - or! Ex -cel - si - or!"

8. A trav - 'ler, by the faith - ful hound, Half bur - ied in the

8. A trav - 'ler, by the faith - ful hound, Half bur - ied in the

snow was found, Still grasp - ing in his hand of ice_____ *f*

snow was found, Still grasp - ing in his hand of ice_____ That

That ban - ner with the

ban - ner with the strange de - vice, That ban - ner with the

strange de - vice, "Ex - cel - si - or! Ex - cel - si -

strange de - vice, "Ex - cel - si - or! Ex - cel - si -

- or!" 9. There in the twi - light

- or!" 9. There in the twi - light

Excelsior!

Excelsior!

Excelsior!

1. The shades of night were falling fast,
   As thro' an Alpine village pass'd
   A youth, who bore 'mid snow and ice
   A banner, with the strange device,
      'Excelsior! Excelsior!'

2. His brow was sad, his eye beneath
   Flash'd like a falchion from its sheath,
   And like a silver clarion rung
   The accents of that unknown tongue,
      'Excelsior! Excelsior!'

3. In happy homes he saw the light
   Of household fires gleam warm and bright,
   Above, the spectral glaciers shone,
   And from his lips escap'd a groan,
      'Excelsior! Excelsior!'

4. 'Try not the pass,' the old man said,
   Dark low'rs the tempest overhead,
   The roaring torrent is deep and wide,
   And loud that clarion voice replied,
      'Excelsior! Excelsior!'

5. 'O stay, O stay,' the maiden said,
   'And rest thy weary head upon this breast,'
   A tear stood in his bright blue eye,
   But still he answer'd, with a sigh,
      'Excelsior! Excelsior!'

6. 'Beware the pine-tree's wither'd branch,
   Beware the awful avalanche,'
   This was the peasant's last goodnight;
   A voice replied, far up the height,
      'Excelsior! Excelsior!'

7. At break of day, as heavenward,
   The pious monks of San Bernard
   Utter'd an oft-repeated pray'r,
   A voice cried thro' the startled air,
      'Excelsior! Excelsior!'

8. A trav'ler, by the faithful hound,
   Half buried in the snow was found,
   Still grasping in his hand of ice
   That banner with the strange device,
      'Excelsior! Excelsior!'

9. There in the twilight cold and grey,
   Lifeless, but beautiful he lay,
   And from the sky serene and far,
   A voice fell like a falling star,
      'Excelsior! Excelsior!'

'A trumpet call to the energies of youth,' Dr Oliver Wendell Holmes called it. No more thrilling testimonial to Victorian optimism exists. Inspiration came to Longfellow in the form of a heading to a New York newspaper: the State seal, a shield with rising sun and the motto, 'Excelsior!' The poet's famous conception took shape instantly: the boy ascending an Alp bearing the banner inscribed, 'Upward Hope', the symbol of youth striving to achieve nobler things, maybe not succeeding in this life but receiving his reward in the next.

Longfellow was piqued by critics who considered that his sentiments did him more credit than his Latin and that a cry of 'Excelsus' or 'Ad Excelsiore' would have been more appropriate. He did not claim poetic licence and the demands of metre, but explained that his text had been 'Scopus meus excelsior est' (My goal is higher), adding unconvincingly, 'You will perceive that "Excelsior", an adjective of the comparative degree, is used adverbially; a use justified by the best Latin writers.'

M. W. Balfe's setting is one of a number to exploit the poem. It is incomparably the best. So dramatic is it that certain passages are almost too good to be true. Notice the warning diminished sevenths, 'Try not the pass . . . Dark low'rs the tempest overhead, etc.', dispelled by the major, assertive 'Excelsior!' Later the chromatic imitative treatment of 'Excelsior!' is magnificent, as are the hint of hunting horns and the 'religioso' parallel fifths of the pious monks. The dramatic restatement of 'Excelsior!' breaks through again in the major. The sequential treatment of the title motto to form a very effective coda is also noteworthy. All the same, this is not a song to be studied on the page where its weaknesses are all too obvious. The sceptical have only to hear it in performance to be converted. Excelsior, indeed.

Balfe set many other favourite poems by Longfellow, among them 'The Arrow and the Song', 'Goodnight, Goodnight Beloved', 'The Day is Done' and 'Trust Her Not (Beware!)' which has the exclamatory stanza:

> I know a maiden fair to see,
> Take care!
> She can both false and friendly be,
> Beware! Beware!
> Trust her not,
> She is fooling thee! *Beware!*

The Moon Has Raised Her Lamp Above

(from *The Lily of Killarney*)

DUET

Written by JOHN OXENFORD

Composed by SIR JULIUS BENEDICT

1. The moon has rais'd her lamp a-bove, To light the way to thee, my love, to light____ the way____ to

The Moon Has Raised Her Lamp Above

thee,_____ my love; Her rays up-on the wa-ters play, to

tell me eyes more bright than they Are watch-ing thro' the

night_____ Are watch-ing thro' the night!_____ I come,_____ I

come,_____ my heart's_____ de-light_____ I come,_____ I

come,_____ my heart's_____ de-light,_____ I come,_____ I

come,_____ I come, my heart's de - light!

I come, I come, my heart's de - light!

I come, I come my heart's de - light!

TENOR
2. On hill_____ and dale_____ the moon - beams

fall,_____ And spread_____ their sil – ver light_____ o'er

The Moon Has Raised Her Lamp Above

all,   But those____ bright eyes   I

BASS   But those bright eyes I soon shall see, Re - serve their pur - est

soon____ shall see,   Re - serve their light____

light for me,   re - serve their pur - est light, re - serve their

____ for me,_ Me thinks____ they now,____ they

pur - est light for me.____ Me thinks they now in - vite!____

colla voce   *pp*   *a tempo*

353

The Moon Has Raised Her Lamp Above

The Moon Has Raised Her Lamp Above

1. The moon has rais'd her lamp above,
    To light the way to thee, my love;
Her rays upon the waters play,
    To tell me eyes more bright than they
Are watching thro' the night!
    I come, my heart's delight.

2. On hill and dale the moonbeams fall,
    And spread their silver light o'er all,
But those bright eyes I soon shall see,
    Reserve their purest light for me.
Methinks they now invite!
    I come, my heart's delight!

A charming piece for baritone and tenor, this comes off extremely well in performance. The two voices are well differentiated, the baritone passionate and the tenor lyrical, decorating the stronger line.

John Oxenford (1812–1877) was almost completely self-educated. He was articled to a solicitor and then tried financial journalism. His leanings were towards continental literature, and he turned his passion into a profession, becoming a translator. The theatre, too, fascinated him, and he gained a reputation as a dramatist. He was dramatic critic of *The Times* for over a quarter of a century, but it is reported that he was so kind-hearted that he could not bear to hurt anyone's feelings by adverse notices. Poet, too, lyricist and music critic, he appears to have been the complete man of letters. Among his libretti was that for the opera, *The Lily of Killarney*, much acclaimed at the time.

There is a note upon the composer, Sir Julius Benedict, on page 164.

Goodnight, Goodnight, Beloved

Written by H. W. Longfellow

Composed by Ciro Pinsuti

Arranged by H. Elliot Button

Goodnight, Goodnight, Beloved

Goodnight, Goodnight, Beloved

Goodnight, Goodnight, Béloved

Goodnight, Goodnight, Beloved

Goodnight, Goodnight, Beloved

Goodnight, goodnight, beloved!
I come to watch o'er thee!
To be near thee, alone is peace for me!
Goodnight, beloved!
I come to watch o'er thee!

Thine eyes are stars of morning,
Thy lips are crimson flowers.
Goodnight, beloved, while I count the
    weary hours.
Goodnight, beloved!
I come to watch o'er thee!

This final section of duets and part songs contains some real gems, as well as Gems. Pinsuti's setting of 'Goodnight, Goodnight, Beloved!' is no exception; it is one of his best works. Each time the original theme returns, it gains new strength from the way it is represented. The lyricism of the passage, 'Thine eyes are stars of morning,' is quite delightful, and there is an unexpected bonus in the chromatic coda. The arrangement printed here, for alto, two tenors and bass, is not the original, but chosen for its effectiveness.

Il Cavaliere Ciro Ercole Pinsuti (1829–1888) was a precocious little boy, an honorary member of the Accademia Filharmonica in Rome at the age of eleven. An English M.P. befriended him, encouraged his studies—including a period with Rossini—and brought him to England. At the age of nineteen, Pinsuti opened his career as a fashionable singing teacher. He composed three operas and collected a number of Italian decorations. From 1856 he was a professor of singing at the Royal Academy of Music, and counted Patti among his pupils. His part songs were great favourites with English singing societies, and he wrote over 300 vocal pieces. One of them, 'I Fear No Foe', was a favourite among the more virile baritones.

Sweet and Low

Written by ALFRED, LORD TENNYSON

Composed by SIR JOSEPH BARNBY

Sweet and Low

Sweet and Low

371

Sweet and Low

1. Sweet and low, sweet and low,
   Wind of the western sea,
   Low, low, breathe and blow,
   Wind of the western sea!
   Over the rolling waters go,
   Come from the dying moon, and blow,
   Blow him again to me;
   While my little one, while my pretty
       one sleeps.

2. Sleep and rest, sleep and rest,
   Father will come to thee soon;
   Rest, rest, on mother's breast,
   Father will come to thee soon;
   Father will come to his babe in the nest,
   Silver sails all out of the west
   Under the silver moon:
   Sleep, my little one, sleep my pretty
       one, sleep.

Always much admired, this sugared masterpiece makes considerable demands upon its singers. Enormous diaphragms are required to sustain the long piano vocal lines with full conviction, but once mastered this song cannot fail to delight audiences as much now as it did in 1863. As with the previous part-song, the arrangement here, for male-voice quartet, has been chosen as more characteristic of the piece than the frequently heard version for soprano, alto, tenor and bass. The lyric is a snatch from Tennyson's 'Medley', *The Princess*.

Sir Joseph Barnby (1838–1896) was the son of an organist. He became a chorister at York Minster, and, in the true tradition of the prodigy, found himself cathedral organist and choirmaster at the age of twelve. As his reputation grew, he formed his own choir and, in the words of Grove, 'He was appointed precentor of Eton in 1875—a post of the highest importance in the musical education of the upper classes.' Later he achieved the position of Principal of the Guildhall School of Music. His style, exemplified in his large corpus of sacred music, part-songs and 246 hymns, has come to epitomise, so far as choral composition is concerned, Victorian musical style.